The Avid®
Digital
Editing Room
Handbook

2nd EDITION

The Avid®
Digital
Editing Room
Handbook

2nd EDITION

Tony Solomons

SILMAN-JAMES PRESS   **LOS ANGELES**

First Silman-James Press Edition

10 9 8 7 6 5 4 3 2 1

Library of Congress Cataloging-in-Publication Data

Solomons, Tony, 1970–
The Avid digital editing room handbook / by Tony Solomons. —
2nd ed.
p.   cm.
1. Motion pictures—Editing—Data processing Handbooks, manuals, etc.
2. Video tapes—Editing—Data processing Handbooks, manuals, etc.   I. Title.
TR899.S65   1999   778.5'235—dc21   99-13152

ISBN 1-879505-48-7 (alk. paper)

Cover design by Wade Lageose

Printed in the United States of America.

SILMAN-JAMES PRESS
1181 Angelo Drive
Beverly Hills, CA 90210

SPECIAL THANKS

I would like to acknowledge Irving Goldworm for introducing me to digital editing systems and my wonderful wife Stacey for her continued encouragement and devotion.

I would also like to thank Avid Technologies, Robert Brakey, Dale Jones, Locals 776 and 771, New Media, Eric Rigney, Teac, and Transoft Networks, Inc. for their support in providing me with information for this edition.

Silman-James Press extends an invitation to readers to comment on this book. We have a responsibility to provide the most accurate and helpful information possible. If there are any areas that you would like the author to explain more thoroughly or if you have suggestions for future editions, please send us your thoughts. This book will be regularly updated as the technologies change and grow.

TABLE OF CONTENTS

INTRODUCTION

A few years ago, I was teaching a graduate-level course on editing. I started my class by distributing a three-page handout on the Avid. It was just a few words of wisdom mixed with some helpful tips and explanations of complicated Avid functions. Mostly it was information that did not exist in the Avid users' guide. I felt like a kid disclosing video-game insider information—if you made Super Mario jump over the special mushroom, you would find the secret shortcut. My editing students responded with as much enthusiasm as you would expect from impassioned video-game enthusiasts.

My guest speaker that night was Dan Hanley. To my surprise, the editor of *Backdraft*, *Ransom*, and *Apollo 13* actually asked if he might have a copy of my handout. At that moment I realized how helpful a book that disclosed all of Super Mario's secrets would be.

In the spring of 1997, I released the first edition of *The Digital Editing Room Handbook*. Nothing could have prepared me for the overwhelming response. The book was quietly released with an advertising budget of zero. Due to the Internet and word of mouth, I sold out every copy of the first run within a few months. Soon I was distributing in Canada, England, France, Germany, Brazil, and Hong Kong. My dilemma then became: print more books or release a new, updated second edition.

Over the past year, many advances have been made in digital editing. Some of you who are working hard on long-term projects may not be aware of what is going on in other cutting rooms. Most of us have experienced the feeling of diving headfirst into the black hole of postproduction only to emerge ten months later to discover that worlds have changed, planets have collided, and Avid has developed eight new versions of its Composer software. The second edition of this book was written to help you bridge that gap.

The Avid Digital Editing Room Handbook is a guide to a smoothly run digital cutting room. This informal, practical reference book provides a comprehensive look at editing on one of today's hottest and most widely used editing system. The book gives clear explanations of:

- Telecine and the 3-2 pulldown process
- Media management and shared storage
- How to configure a feature project
- Digitizing and editing
- Cut lists and EDLs

- Outputs and conforming
- Software version 7.3 and 8.0
- Fibre channel
- DA-88
- Bugs, fixes, work-arounds, tips, and tricks
- Preventive maintenance and much, much more.

This book is intended for avid Avid users with all levels of expertise. Whether you have years of experience or little at all, every digital cutting room should have a copy of this handbook on the shelf. This is the only complete guide to the Avid Digital Editing Room in the universe.

Don't spend valuable time waiting for a telephone representative; look it up in the first editor's guide to the Avid.

CHAPTER 1
THE DIGITAL EDITING ROOM

CHAPTER OUTLINE

How Does It Work?
Telecine Explained: The Exciting 3-2 Pulldown Process

The key to being a successful digital editor is knowing the digital world, the film world, and the video world. The Avid integrates these three worlds into one editing system.

The three worlds each have their own language. It is to your advantage to speak these languages fluently. Mastering the Avid Composer software alone will not prepare an editor to successfully run a feature editing room. Timecode from the video world, key numbers from the film world, and gigabytes from the digital world are not the most exciting or intelligible concepts. However, in the following chapters you will find explanations of the more important concepts from all three worlds and how they work together.

HOW DOES IT WORK?

In my Avid classes, I try to explain everything in an easy-to-understand way. I start by explaining how the Avid actually works. It is important to understand the total picture before diving into what button does what. To this end, I have come up with an analogy for the Avid that seems to work for most people.

The Avid has two main areas: the computer and the media storage drives. Imagine that the computer is a big house and the media drive is the garage that is connected to the house by a car port. The house consists of many rooms (bins). Now imagine that master clips are empty picture frames on the walls of these rooms.

Still with me? The picture frames (master clips) come in all shapes and sizes and may be arranged on the walls of your house in any way you choose. The photographs that fill the picture frames (media) live in boxes in the garage. The garage could fit one car or two cars, just as media drives come in different sizes (4-gig, 9-gig, etc.). These photographs magically appear in the picture frames every time you walk into a room.

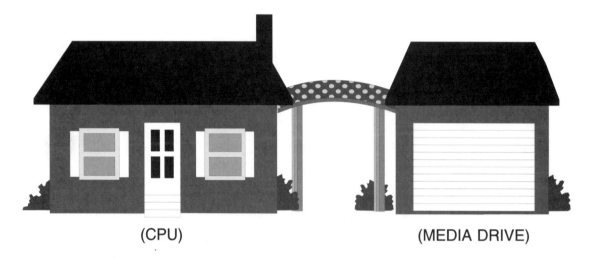

(CPU)   (MEDIA DRIVE)

As you decorate each room in your house (edit), the picture frames are arranged in a specific order on the wall. The photographs in the frames provide your aesthetic inspiration. Technically, if the garage burned down, you could still arrange the picture frames on your walls. However, the absence of these photographs would make it difficult to decide which picture looks best next to another.

The Avid records your edit decisions in an arrangement called a sequence. This sequence of joined master clips exists even without the media that accompanies it. The media is what you see and hear; it is the moving images and the audio. The media is separate and different from the numerical information contained within a clip, a sequence, or a list of edit decisions. You could play and edit a sequence without the presence of media. However, you won't be able to see or hear anything, but all the numbers will be there. If you understand this theory, almost everything else on the Avid makes more sense.

Master clips, sequences, and bins are stored as numerical information in the project folder on your computer's hard drive. Your project is an *original*, and the most important information. All of your edit decisions and hard work are stored in your project folder on the computer's hard drive. It would not be good if you lost this information. You can lose your media without disastrous consequences, but never lose your project! This is the main reason for project backups (see Chapter 13, **Saving Your Work**).

Media, digitized audio and video, is different and separate from the material in the project folder. *Media* is considered expendable because it is not *original material*. The *original materials* are the actual negative and sound rolls of which you have several copies in the form of a workprint and mag, a telecine tape, and digitized media.

TELECINE EXPLAINED: THE EXCITING 3-2 PULLDOWN PROCESS

Telecine is the process by which film is transferred to videotape. Film runs at a speed of exactly 24 frames per second. There are 24 frames of film in every second of a movie. Each frame of film consists of *one* segment. Videotape runs at a speed of 29.97 frames per second; however, it is often referred to as running at 30 frames per second. There are 30 frames of video in one second of videotape. Each frame of video consists of *two* segments called fields. There are two fields in one frame of video. Each pair of fields contain almost exactly the same information.

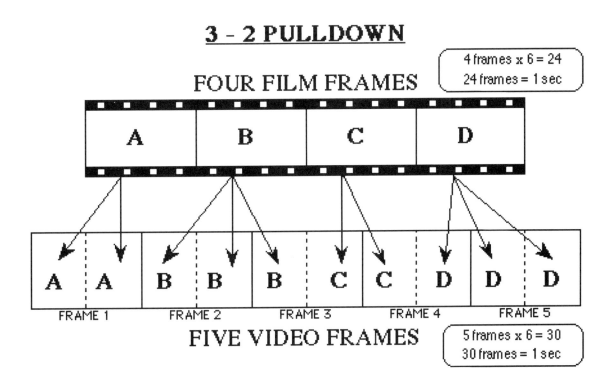

When transferring film to video, we are trying to shove 24 frames into 60 fields per second. This conversion is known as the "3-2 Pulldown" or the "2-3 Pulldown."

The 3-2 pulldown process works as follows: The information from the first frame of film, the "A" frame, is copied onto the first two fields of video. This first video frame now contains two identical fields copied from the "A" film frame. The second frame of film, the "B" frame, is copied onto the 3rd, 4th, and 5th field of video. The "B" frame is copied onto three fields rather than two. Therefore, 1½ video frames contain the "B" film frame information.

So far the information from the first two frames of film has been copied, or pulled, onto two (2), then three (3) fields of video. This is the 2-3 pulldown process. We are not done yet.

This process is repeated for the third and fourth frames of film. The third frame of film is copied onto two fields of video, and the fourth frame of film is copied onto three fields of video. The third frame of film is copied onto the 6th and 7th field of video. The fourth frame of film is copied onto the 8th, 9th, and 10th field of video. After repeating four film frames and five video frames six times, you end up with one second of film time or one second of video time; whichever way you look at it, a second is a second.

Now that you completely understand the 3-2 pulldown process, let me burst your bubble. The 3-2 pulldown works if the film is running at a speed of 24 fps and the video is running at a speed of 30 fps. But as we have already established, video runs at a speed of 29.97 fps. I know what you are thinking, "Why have I just wasted time learning a theory that does not work?" I will tell you why. If you slowed down the film to run slightly slower than 24 fps, just as video runs at a speed of slightly under 30 fps, the 3-2 pulldown process works.

The 3-2 pulldown process works because the telecine house slows the speed of the Rank. The Rank, similar to a projector, is the device that runs the film during the film-to-tape transfer process. The speed differential between 30 fps and 29.97 fps for video is duplicated for film by the Rank system. Therefore, film is run at a speed of 23.976 during the telecine process.

Since the speed of the film is altered during the telecine process, the Avid compensates by speeding telecine material back up to 24 fps, as long as you digitize with the pulldown set at "x 0.99." The audio interface on the Avid has a Pulldown switch for digitizing at "x 1.00" or "x 0.99." The Pulldown switch should be set to "x 0.99" for digitizing any material that has been through the telecine process. Setting the Pulldown switch to "x 0.99" actually speeds the telecine tape back up to the equivalent of 24 fps. The "x 1.00" setting does not affect the video or audio frame rate, therefore, this setting is used for digitizing any material that has not gone through the telecine process.

TECHNICAL JUNK: Audio run through the telecine process is converted from a frequency of 44.1 kHz to 43.056 kHz.

CHAPTER 2
AVID HARDWARE

CHAPTER OUTLINE

An editor need not know everything about the inner workings of all the hardware items on a digital editing system. Certainly it is to your advantage to learn as much as possible. However, the production should understand that professional technical support is essential on a digital show: Many complicated computer software and hardware items are included in your Avid. Several of these items may malfunction or fail during normal usage over an extended period of time. The following are some of the basic hardware items you should be familiar with.

PLATFORM - The platform is the computer operating system and the brain behind a digital editing system. An Avid digital editing system utilizes a customized Macintosh computer as its platform. The Quadra 950 was a popular platform for the Avid in past years. The Power PC Macintosh computers are preferable now due to the faster-performing chip. The difference between a Macintosh computer and an Avid is some additional hardware and the editing software. Avid installs cards into the Macs, such as the NuVista Card, the ABVB (Avid Broadcast Video Board), the JPEG Compression board, and the E-Board, in addition to the Composer software. Avid Technology has also developed a consumer line of editing software programs for Windows NT and Macs.

> **TECHNICAL JUNK:** The NuVista Card delivers a 640 x 480 video signal compared to the newer ABVB board's 720 x 486 signal.

> **WARNING!** The inside of your computer is sensitive to electrostatic currents. A protective grounding wrist strap must be worn while handling any of the interior parts of your system. This inexpensive accessory looks like an elastic wristband connected to a long wire that is attached to the designated grounding point on your computer. Refer to your hardware specifications for grounding instructions.

MONITORS - The Avid digital editing system utilizes two computer monitors and a third NTSC monitor. The left computer monitor is called the *bin monitor* and the right computer monitor is called the *edit monitor*. The NTSC monitor displays a video signal fed by the Avid. It is activated by entering big-screen mode for software versions older than 6.0. For Composer versions 6.0 and above, the third monitor remains full screen (see Shift-Big-Screen, Chapter 16).

Calibrate your NTSC monitors for color and luminance before starting a project. Play a tape with good quality bars and make sure that the white area is white, the colors look even, and the gray scale is visible in the lower right. If you are not familiar enough to recognize a correct representation of bars, ask your system supplier to calibrate the monitor. If you do not have a tape with bars available, the Video Output Tool can send SMPTE Bars to the NTSC monitor.

> **REMEMBER!** Make sure to set your Monitor setting in the Control Panel to the best picture quality.

DECKS - A digital editing system digitizes from a videotape format. BetaSP, ¾-inch, and S-VHS with timecode are the three most common formats. Whichever type of deck you have, check that it is in working order before digitizing. Many technical problems arise from deck malfunctions or the user's lack of knowledge. Become familiar with all the deck settings and functions.

> **TIP:** A certain major electronics company (which will remain nameless) manufactures a VHS deck that has an annoying quirk. The deck automatically spits out any tape for which the record tab has been removed. If you encounter this notorious deck, place a piece of tape over the record inhibitor so the deck can accept the tape.

KEYBOARD AND MOUSE - The keyboard and mouse are standard Mac items. Avid adds colorful keys to the basic keyboard to make it easier to identify the buttons. If your keyboard does not have the colorful keys, call Avid and get the special stickers to customize your keyboard.

> **WARNING!** Unplugging the keyboard or mouse while your computer is running may cause your system to run incorrectly.

AUDIO

SPEAKERS AND AMPLIFIERS - The Avid comes with two small, self-powered Roland speakers. Alternative speakers may be substituted, but an external amplifier is necessary for any speaker that does not have a built-in amplifier.

Consumer audio and video equipment usually carries an unbalanced audio signal. Professional audio and video equipment usually carries a balanced audio signal. The difference between unbalanced and balanced audio is similar to the difference between two-prong plugs and three-prong grounded plugs. Unbalanced audio utilizes two-prong connectors (it looks like one prong) where balanced audio has three prongs and each carries a slightly different audio frequency.

The Avid outputs a balanced audio signal. A balanced amplifier should be used in conjunction with the Avid. If you channel balanced audio through an unbalanced amplifier, the signal will diminish substantially; converters are available that can boost audio signals as they travel from a balanced source through an unbalanced device. Consult your system provider regarding your amplifier specifications.

MIXERS - A mixer is not a standard piece of equipment on a digital editing system. Most people use one, and I highly recommend adding this to your setup. The Avid is limited in its ability to boost audio levels as they enter the system. A mixer can amplify audio signals from decks, CD players, and other external devices. CD players often cannot provide adequate audio levels for digitizing. Connecting a mixer between the CD player and the Avid would give you the flexibility to boost, lower, EQ, and filter audio as it enters the system.

ROUTERS - Some of the better rental houses include a router with each system. This device replaces a traditional patch panel. Rather than sporting a mound of spaghetti behind your system, routers make it easier to patch decks to and from the Avid. All of the external devices attach to the router, which distributes each signal. The dial menu on the face of this device allows you to design the patching configuration. Different types of routers enable you to select the signal destination (destination-based router) or the source device (origination-based router).

STORAGE

Digital editing systems store media on different types of storage drives (a.k.a. media drives). The following section describes these devices.

CHASSIS - A connection device that attaches to the computer. It holds two R-Mags.

R-MAG - A removable external hard drive that mounts into a chassis. It contains the media for a project (it looks like a suitcase).

FIXED DRIVE - An external hard drive that connects directly to the computer. It contains the media for a project.

TOWERS - External hard drives that, connected together, act like one large fixed drive. Towers generally perform better than fixed drives.

STORAGE EXPANDER - An external device that connects additional drives to an existing tower. It looks just like a 9-gig drive.

> **WARNING!** Media drives may burn out as a result of normal usage. It is not uncommon to lose one or more media drives over an extended period.

> **WARNING!** Each drive on your system needs a unique ID number. You cannot have two hard drives with the same ID on the same bus.

> **WARNING!** Always shut down the system before you attach, detach, or check any cable or device connection. Altering a hardware connection to a system that is on may cause a crash.

ZIP DRIVE - An additional internal or external drive used to store information. It uses 100-megabyte Zip disks. Zip disks look similar to 3.5-inch disks but may contain approximately 67 times more information.

JAZZ DRIVE (RECOMMENDED FOR BACKING UP YOUR PROJECT) - An additional internal or external drive used to store information. It uses 1-gigabyte Jazz disks. Iomega also manufactures a 2-gigabyte Jazz drive that reads 1-gig and 2-gig Jazz disks.

OPTICAL DRIVE - An additional drive used to store information or media. Optical disks are similar to media drives, except they are smaller and much slower. Some people use optical drives to store audio files or small amounts of video.

See Chapter 10, **Fibre Channel,** for descriptions of fibre hardware products.

CABLES

XLR CABLE - Primarily used as balanced audio cables, XLR cables connect audio to and from the Avid. The audio inputs and outputs on your audio interface are XLR connectors. Some of the other components in your system, the video deck and DAT player, utilize XLR connections for audio. XLR cables may be patched to various audio adapters. However, whenever patching balanced audio with unbalanced audio cables, severe loss of amplitude occurs.

BNC CABLE (a.k.a. coaxial cable) - Primarily used as a video cable. Connects video to and from the Avid.

RCA CABLE - Used as an audio and/or video cable. Connects audio and video to and from VHS recorders, CD players, tape recorders, and other devices. RCA cables carry unbalanced audio signals.

> **TIP:** Always keep a supply of various adapters for connections between any configuration of XLR, RCA, or BNC cables. Purchase the male and female versions of each adapter.

BATTERY BACKUP

UPS (HIGHLY RECOMMENDED) - An Uninterrupted Power Supply is a battery-backup device that all your Avid equipment should be plugged into. In the event of a power failure, spike, or fluctuation, the UPS will deliver an uninterrupted stream of power to all your equipment. The device will power your computer long enough for you to back up the project and shut down.

CHAPTER 3
AVID COMPANION SOFTWARE PROGRAMS

CHAPTER OUTLINE

Composer
PC Exchange
SCSI Probe
Norton Utilities
> Norton Disk Doctor
> Speed Disk
Avid Drive Utility
Avid Log Exchange
Compact Pro

In addition to several hardware items that are added to a regular Macintosh computer to convert it into an Avid digital editing system, several software programs are also necessary. The following are some of the software programs that you should become familiar with.

COMPOSER SOFTWARE - *Film Composer* and *Media Composer* are the two main operating software applications for the Avid digital editing system. *Film Composer* is designed primarily for 24-fps film projects. *Media Composer* is designed primarily for 30-fps video projects. These are the application programs with which you edit your projects.

PC EXCHANGE - PC Exchange is a software program that allows a Macintosh computer to recognize PC-formatted disks. Your computer will not be able to recognize non-Macintosh disks without PC Exchange installed and activated. Check the status of PC Exchange from the Extension Manager.

SCSI PROBE - SCSI Probe is a software program that recognizes and mounts external devices connected to the computer. It is used to mount drives onto the desktop.

If you connect a new device to your computer, the device icon may not automatically appear on the desktop after restart. Open SCSI Probe and select Update. This will force the computer to double-check all devices connected to the computer. Select Mount and hope that the device's icon appears. If not, check the cable connections and try again.

WARNING! SCSI Probe may be incompatible and may cause problems in conjunction with Transoft's FibreNet (see Channel 10, Fibre Channel).

REMEMBER! Never add, remove, or change any connections or cables on your computer while it is running. Always shut down your computer before modifying any cable connections to it. Patching or unpatching cables to your system while it is running could damage your drives and delete your media.

NORTON UTILITIES

NORTON DISK DOCTOR - Norton Disk Doctor is the part of Norton Utilities that analyzes computer files, reports problems, suggests solutions, and performs some fixes (see Chapter 20, **Maintenance**).

SPEED DISK - Included within Norton Utilities, Speed Disk optimizes drives by rearranging data into less fragmented patterns. This application is recommended for defragmenting your hard drive. However, do not use Speed Disk on media drives unless you want to destroy all the media on the drive. Media files are too large for Speed Disk to move (see Optimizing Your Hard Drive, Chapter 20).

WARNING! Do not use Speed Disk on media drives.

AVIDdrive UTILITY - Avid has its own utility program that is installed on every system. This program mounts, installs, partitions, labels, formats, and erases drives. Make sure you know how to use AVIDdrive Utility before performing any of its functions. Certain functions may erase media from a drive.

TIP: Avid recommends keeping AVIDdrive Utility running in the background with SCSI Media Share. If the Mount All function is disabled, AVIDdrive Utility will enable you to mount partitions without restarting the computer. If you notice that Norton is finding an increased amount of problems as a result of running AVIDdrive Utility, discontinue using AVIDdrive Utility to mount partitions. Restarting the computer is always a risk-free option for mounting partitions onto the desktop; however, some editors find this work-around to be an inconvenience.

WARNING! The install function in AVIDdrive Utility 1.4 may cause a loss of data—this version of the utility has a bug. Do not use the install function when partitions appear gray.

AVID LOG EXCHANGE - Avid Log Exchange is a software program that converts the "logs" you receive from the telecine house into Avid Log Exchange files (a.k.a. ALE files). You can't import Flex or Evertz or other log files into your Composer. The Composer software does not recognize foreign log files. You must first convert these files into ALE files (see Chapter 8, **Digitizing**).

COMPACT PRO - Compact Pro is a software program that compresses a file or files into a new, smaller, compacted file. The new compacted file contains fewer megs. The process of compacting files using Compact Pro is like packing up all your bulky winter clothing to make room in your closet for your summer duds. You cram all your wool sweaters and ski jacket into a cardboard box and store it in the basement. When fall arrives, the musty clothes come back to the closet. Double-clicking on a compacted file will restore the contents to the original expanded configuration.

Compact Pro also has a feature that can recognize only those files that have been modified since a specific date. This handy program becomes very useful while backing up your project's files (see Chapter 13, **Saving Your Work**).

MSSCANNER - (See Chapter 9, **SCSI Media Share**)

FIBRENET - (See Chapter 10, **Fibre Channel**)

CHAPTER 4
MAC BASICS

CHAPTER OUTLINE

The Avid digital editing system operates from a Macintosh computer. The computer, or platform, is the brain behind the Avid. Therefore, it is necessary to understand the computer first, then the software that runs on it. This chapter is designed to explain several Mac basics that directly relate to your Avid.

I highly recommend becoming as familiar as possible with Macintosh computers. Learning a new digital editing system is hard enough without doubling the challenge. If you are inexperienced using Macintosh computers, take a quick computer class. Some of the larger national computer stores offer one-day basic, intermediate, and specialized computer classes. These classes will prove invaluable as you learn the Avid. The more you know about the Avid platform, the better!

DESKTOP - The desktop is the actual work area for the computer. It is shown in the left monitor (a.k.a. bin monitor) on an Avid. The desktop contains icons and a menu bar at the top. Pretend it is your desk. The desktop would be the top of your desk and the desk's drawers would be represented by the icons that appear on the right side of the monitor. Most of your files should be in the drawers, but you may place folders and files on your desktop while you work.

DESKTOP

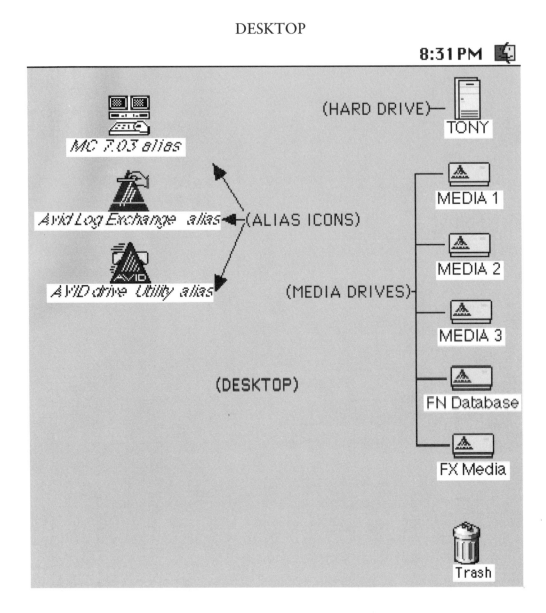

STARTUP KEYBOARD FUNCTIONS - You can perform several functions as you start up your computer. The following chart details a few helpful startup keystroke functions. Each keystroke combination should be held down while the computer starts up until a dialog box indicates that the function has been initiated (see Chapter 20, **Maintenance,** for a complete explanation).

FUNCTION	KEYSTROKE
Rebuild the Desktop	⌘–Option
Customize Extension Manager	Space Bar
Turn Extensions Off	Shift
Zap the P-Ram	Option–⌘–P–R

- Rebuilding the desktop refreshes the computer's understanding of what is sitting on the desktop.

- Customizing the Extensions Manager allows you activate or deactivate extensions from a menu while the computer is booting up.

- You can turn off all the extensions as you start your computer by holding down the shift key.

- Zapping the P-Ram can be considered a computer enema (see Chapter 20, **Maintenance**).

SYSTEM FOLDER - The system folder contains items that operate the basic functions of a Mac. The primary operating drive, or startup drive, must contain a system folder. The Control Panel, DigiSetup, Extensions, and Apple Menu are all items contained within the System Folder that you should be familiar with.

EXTENSIONS - Extensions are supportive files that add functionality to computers. Select the specific extensions you want to activate through the Extension Manager in the Control Panel. If you do not have an Extension Manager in your Control Panel, manually drag the superfluous extensions from the Extensions folder into an Extensions (Disabled) folder. The Extension Manager automatically creates an Extensions (Disabled) folder for superfluous extensions. However, if you do not have an Extension Manager, create your own Extensions (Disabled) folder. Changes in the Extension Manager settings or Extensions folder only take effect after a restart. Be careful while installing new programs onto your computer so that new extensions do not conflict with the operation of the computer because some extensions are not compatible with others. If you experience a problem due to possible conflicting extensions, restart your computer without the extensions turned on. To do this, hold the Shift key down while you boot up the computer.

WARNING! Some extensions are not compatible with others and may affect the operation of the computer. Conflicting extensions may cause your computer to freeze upon startup.

CONTROL PANEL - The Control Panel contains items such as the Extensions Manager, PC Exchange, Monitors & Sound settings, and Startup Disk allocation.

DIGI SETUP - The DigiSetup file is an Avid audio settings file that lives in the System folder. This file may become corrupt during the course of a project. You will experience constant audio distortion while playing a clip or sequence when the DigiSetup file is corrupt. This file can be easily rebuilt by trashing the corrupt file and then restarting your system from scratch. The Composer software will automatically rebuild the DigiSetup file if one does not exist in the system folder.

Depending on your Composer version, the DigiSetup file may be located either in the System folder or the Preferences folder within the System folder.

APPLE MENU - The Apple Menu is provided solely for your convenience. It allows you quicker access to some of your favorite and most frequently used files and applications. The Apple Menu appears on the top left of the desktop and is recognizable by an apple icon on the menu bar. Select and hold the Apple icon to reveal the items in the menu.

To place an item in the Apple Menu, make an alias of any application, file, or folder and place the alias in the Apple Menu folder located in the System Folder. An alias is made by selecting ⌘–M while the designated item's icon is highlighted.

TIP: An alias does not contain any parts of the item it represents. Deleting an alias does not affect the original file, folder, or application. For your convenience, most Avid systems will have an alias of the Composer software on the desktop. If there is no software alias on the desktop, make one.

TIP: The keystroke function ⌘–W will automatically close an open folder or file on the desktop. The keystroke function Option–⌘–W will automatically close all open folders and files on the desktop. If you are searching for a folder or file on the desktop and you do not want to have a bunch of open folders crowding up the desktop while you look, hold down the Option key while you open a folder. This will cause the previous folder to close.

RAM (MEMORY) ALLOCATION FOR COMPOSER

All computer programs require a certain amount of available RAM in order to function. Your computer comes with RAM already built in. You can see the amount of built-in RAM by pulling down the Apple Menu to reveal About This Computer while in Finder mode. Not all of the built-in RAM is available to you. As soon as the computer is turned on, the system software uses some of the RAM. The remaining unused RAM is available for other programs.

The Composer software requires a certain amount of available RAM in order to operate properly. Your computer must have enough built-in RAM available to launch and operate the Composer software. The Composer software may open with a limited amount of available RAM, but some of the Composer features will not work due to a RAM shortage. The Composer application Information Window illustration below suggests a minimum of 80 megabytes of RAM for normal operation, but this is not enough RAM to properly operate the 7.0 Composer software. Avid recommends allocating approximately 200 megabytes to the 7.0 Composer software. Make sure that your computer is equipped with enough RAM for the system software, the Composer software, and any shared storage software you may be operating. I recommend installing more than 210 megabytes of total RAM for 7.0 systems and above.

COMPOSER APPLICATION INFORMATION WINDOW

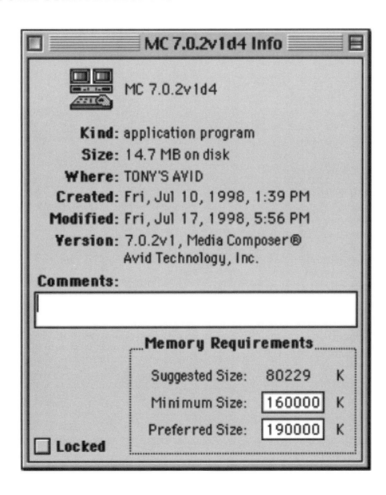

CHANGING COMPOSER'S MEMORY ALLOCATION

STEP BY STEP

1) Quit out of the Composer software.

2) Locate the Composer application icon in the Composer application folder.

3) Highlight the Composer icon.

4) Select ⌘–I to view the application's Information Window.

5) Change the preferred size to 190000. The minimum size is less important and should remain a smaller number than the preferred size. (Consult your system provider or Avid for the appropriate memory allocation for your Composer version.)

6) Close the Information Window and launch the Composer software.

REMEMBER! An application's allocated memory can not be changed while the application is running.

CHAPTER 5
THE MEDIA

CHAPTER OUTLINE

The Avid essentially utilizes two different types of files: The first is the numerical information contained within the project, the second is the media files. Media is the digitized audio and video components utilized by your digital editing system.

Digital editing systems use media in conjunction with numerical information, allowing you to see and hear the material input onto your drives. These drives used to contain the media, called media drives, are separate from the computer's internal hard drive. The media is what you see and hear; it is the moving images and the audio. The Composer software does not rely on the presence of this media. Technically, you can edit your project without media on your drives by arranging the hollow master clips into a list of edit decisions. Realistically, without the media, the absence of audio and video makes it difficult to be creative.

THE MEDIA FACTORY (How Is Media Made?)

Media is created in several different ways. The most common is during digitizing. As you digitize your material into the Avid, the audio and video portions are stored onto your media drives as media files. Media files are much larger than text files. Therefore, your media drives may fill fairly quickly.

TIP: If your media drives reach full capacity, you may experience several technical problems. Media drives should never be filled to capacity. They require a buffer zone of several megabytes. There is no written rule for a safe maximum drive capacity. However, for drives of one gigabyte and larger, I recommend leaving at least 20 to 80 megabytes empty on each partition of a drive at all times. Check the folder heading to determine individual media folder capacities.

MEDIA IS CREATED BY

> Digitizing
> > *Digitizing video creates 1 media file.*
> > *Digitizing video and 1 channel of audio creates 2 media files.*
> > *Digitizing video and 2 channels of audio creates 3 media files.*
> Rendering Effects and Titles
> Importing Quicktime Files and Rendering
> Audio Mixdowns
> Titles and Graphics

NO MEDIA IS CREATED BY

> Duplicating or Moving Sequences
> Duplicating or Moving Clips
> Creating Subclips
> Generating EDLs or Lists
> Creating or Moving Bins
> Saving Your Project

MEDIA DATABASE

The Media Database is a text file that lives with the media in each external drive. It is the road map used by the Composer software to find where each individual piece of media resides. External media drives may be separated into partitions. Each partition that contains media also contains a Media Database file. Since the quantity of media in each partition may change, the Media Database is continually updated to represent the current media inventory. As new media is created, the Media Database file rewrites itself, indicating the change to that particular partition. This busy Media Database file may become corrupt. Corrupt Media Database files may prohibit the Composer software from launching. Deleting corrupt Media Database files may correct this problem (see Chapter 20, **Maintenance**).

MEDIA DATABASE AND MEDIA FILES BEFORE 7.0

	CDA01.AF3378E5_AF16680D	5.2 MB
	175v040A01.AF13894C_AF13...	4.8 MB
	CDA01.AF33788F_AF16680D	3.8 MB
	Media Database	85K

The media database has changed slightly in Composer version 7.0 and later. The function is similar, but the information is stored in a pair of files rather than just one file. The new design allows the Composer software to launch more quickly. One other difference is that the newer files have less-intelligible names.

MEDIA DATABASE AND MEDIA FILES SINCE 7.0

Name	Size
msmMac.pmr	136K
msmOMFI.mdb	544K
030A01.B1DCE4DA_B1DCD231.omf	6.7 MB
030V01.B1DCE4DA_B1DCD231.omf	37.3 MB
030A01.B1DCE354_B1DCD231.omf	5.3 MB

TIP: A media file on a media drive has a long, meaningless identification number as its name. Part of this name consists of the source tape number. If you modify your log files before digitizing to represent not only the tape number but also the appropriate scene number, this information will appear as the first part of the media file's name (see Selecting a Destination Drive, Chapter 8).

MOVING MEDIA

You may have a reason to move media from one drive to another. If you have over-packed a partition or you are disconnecting a media drive, you may want to move some or all of the media from one drive to another. This is an easy procedure.

STEP BY STEP

1) Select the media files you want to move in the 6.x or OMFI media folder on your media drives.

2) Drag the selected files to the desired destination. The computer will automatically make a copy of a media file when you drag it into another partition.

3) Delete the old media files from their original locations once you are certain the media has been successfully copied.

4) Discard the Media Database files in both the original and designated partition.

TIP: Make sure you do not duplicate media files during the moving process. Duplicate media files are unnecessary and waste valuable drive space. You may want to identify the media you intend to move by labeling it with a distinctive color. Under the label menu, select a color other than black. Move the colored files by following the directions above. The clearly color-coded labels make it easier to identify the media you are moving and deleting.

REMEMBER! Always rebuild the media database file on any partition in which a change has been made (see Rebuilding the Media Database Files, Chapter 20).

WARNING! Do not over-pack any drives or partitions. You should never utilize the total capacity of any drive or partition. Although a 1-gigabyte drive may have the capacity to store one gigabyte of information, the drive must maintain some unused space. A full drive may not have the capacity to rewrite a media database file due to lack of storage space. Other more significant problems may occur due to over-packed drives. Always leave at least 20 to 80 megabytes of unused space on a 1-gigabyte drive.

LOSING MEDIA

Avid users often console each other as a result of a major loss. I often receive a call from a colleague mumbling something like, "I'm so depressed, I lost a 9-gig" or "I can't believe it happened to me." Losing media is a traumatic experience many of us face. The depth of depression is measured by the size of your drive.

Offline is the term used to describe a clip for which the media file(s) is missing. Media may become lost in a few different ways. When a media drive dies or a media file becomes corrupt or you delete a media file, a clip will become offline. Losing media as a result of a drive going south is not the end of the world. It is actually a fairly common occurrence. You may have to re-digitize media during the course of a feature project. However, sometimes a bin may falsely indicate that media is missing (see Troubleshooting Media later in this chapter).

LOCATING MEDIA

For better media file management, a handy Reveal File option under the File menu locates all media files on the Finder level associated with a highlighted master clip. This option was introduced with 7.0.

STEP BY STEP

1) Highlight one master clip in a bin.

2) Select Reveal File from the File menu. The storage partition containing the media associated with that particular master clip will automatically appear on your monitor. The exact media file(s) (video and audio) will appear highlighted on that partition.

TIP: The AppleScript extension must be active for the Reveal File to work.

DUPLICATE MEDIA FILES

The duplicate media file dialog box may appear while the Composer software is starting up.

There are two possible reasons for this message. First, there may be duplicate media files on your media drives. You may have digitized a clip more than once. Sometimes a clip temporarily loses the connection from the media file providing a false "media off-line" message. By re-digitizing this clip, you create a duplicate of the original media file that may show up eventually (see Troubleshooting Media later in this chapter). The second reason for receiving this message may be that the Media Database files are not accurate. The Media Database files inventory all the media on a media drive. These files are continually rewritten while you digitize, move media, delete media, create media, and edit. An inaccurate Media Database file may cause false duplicate media messages.

If you get this message, just click OK and continue. No harm will come if you have duplicate media files, and the Delete Unused Duplicates function does not actually delete anything anyway.

DELETING INDIVIDUAL MEDIA FILES

Audio and video media files are not married together. They may be stored in the same or different media drives. You can delete a clip's media by depressing the Delete key while the clip is highlighted. A dialog box will appear asking if you would like to delete the master clip and/or the media file(s) associated with the clip. If you delete the master clip, the clip will disappear forever. If you choose to delete the associated media file(s), the system will not differentiate between the audio and video files. All the media associated with that clip will be deleted.

You *can* delete a clip's separate video or audio track(s). I can only imagine a few instances in which it might be necessary to delete a portion of the media associated with a clip. If you forget to modify wild track clips before they are digitized, you can delete the superfluous video file later without disturbing the audio file. The same applies for MOS shots that have been digitized with audio tracks. Obviously, digitizing audio tracks for MOS shots is okay, but drive space is valuable, so be careful not to waste it.

Deleting Individual Media Files

STEP BY STEP

   1) Open the Media Tool and display only the media associated with your project.

   Most likely the only media on the media drives are from your project. In the television, trailer, commercial, and music-video industries it is more common to find multiple projects and users on one system.

   2) Highlight the clip in the bin and activate Select Media Relatives from the bin's hamburger menu. A copy of the clip will highlight in the media tool.

   3) Activate the Media Tool window and depress the Delete key on the keyboard to delete the media for the highlighted clip. A dialog box will appear asking you if you would like to delete the video or audio media files associated with this clip. If you delete either the audio or video portion of the clip, the bin will recognize that media is missing from the clip if you reactivate Select Offline Items from the hamburger menu.

TROUBLESHOOTING MEDIA

Media database files inventory all the media on media drives. The media database file is the only non-media file contained within each media drive. These files are continually rewritten. If a piece of media is added or removed from a drive before the Media Database file has a chance to update the current drive inventory, the Media Database file will inaccurately reflect the drive contents. Inaccurate Media Database files will not accurately reflect the exact contents of a drive and may cause clips to falsely appear offline. This is the reason Media Database files must be trashed and remade on a regular basis (see Rebuilding the Media Database Files, Chapter 20). Corrupt Media Database files are quite bothersome and may cause a variety of technical problems.

Sometimes a clip temporarily loses its connection from its media file, providing a false Media Offline message. If the video media file becomes unconnected to a clip, a gray frame with the words Media Offline will fill the clip. The audio media file may also become unconnected to the clip. This is harder to recognize since offline audio tracks are not represented by a gray media offline frame. If you notice audio missing from a clip (you don't hear anything when you play the clip), activate Select Offline items from the bin's hamburger menu. The clip for which the audio is missing will highlight in the bin.

When media seems to have disappeared from a perfectly good clip, there can only be two explanations. Either the media is gone or the computer is confused. First, try to relink the clip to its media. This process forces the computer to take another look to make sure that the media is, in fact, lost.

RELINKING CLIPS

STEP BY STEP

1) Highlight the clip in the bin.

2) Select Relink from the Clip menu.

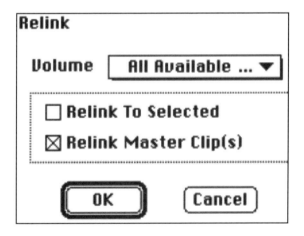

Clips that do not reconnect to associated media files may not necessarily signify the absence of media. Continue with the following procedure.

(See Unlinking, Chapter 8, **Digitizing**.)

REBUILDING THE MEDIA DATABASE FILES

Rebuilding the Media Database files is the best way to restore sanity to your confused clips. This will refresh the computer and reunite any temporarily lost media files with their associated clips (also see Rebuilding the Media Database Files, Chapter 20).

STEP BY STEP

1) Close all software programs.

2) Open each media file folder on the media drives. Find the Media Database file(s). One is in each partition of a media drive.

3) Drag each Media Database file into the trash and empty the trash.

4) Launch the Composer software. If Media Database files do not exist on media drives while initializing the Composer software, the Avid is forced to rebuild the missing files. This process may take a while depending on the density and quantity of media drives connected to your computer.

REMEMBER! If a clip has lost either a video or an audio file, only the missing piece needs to be digitized. Many times audio and video media files are stored separately on different media drives. If one of these drives dies, you may find a group of clips that have lost either their audio or video portion.

CHAPTER 6
FILM DAILIES

CHAPTER OUTLINE

FILM DAILIES

The revolution in digital editing has changed the way in which we edit movies today. Digital editing systems provide instantaneous access to every frame of a movie, the ability to simultaneously share the same material on multiple workstations, and the ability to preview simple to complex opticals. None of these changes have eliminated the *film* editing room. As long as movies are released on film, we will continue to shoot and edit movies on celluloid. Film dailies still have to be synced and screened each day. The footage has to be logged and coded, boxed and organized, and screened and cleaned. Unless celluloid is completely eliminated from the filmmaking process, the protocol for organizing film dailies will remain unchanged.

The digital editing revolution has not eliminated the traditional assistant film editor's duties. Rather, editing rooms have expanded in sophistication and personnel with the addition of the digital assistant editor. In order to be a well-rounded assistant in the digital editing room, it is to your advantage to know as much as possible about film, video, and digital formats. Once you understand the film aspect of a feature, the digital world becomes much clearer. The following chapter outlines the procedures for syncing and organizing film dailies on a feature film.

It is no secret that the name of this book was derived from another editing-room handbook, *The Film Editing Room Handbook* by Norman Hollyn. I recommend Hollyn's book if you are interested in learning more about the nuts and bolts of a film editing room.

THE LAB

Each day of principal photography on a film project, the set delivers the unprocessed film to the lab with the camera reports. The lab develops all of the camera-original negative, but only makes a workprint for those takes that are circled on the camera reports. The workprint is delivered from the lab to the editing room each morning with a lab report attached. The film usually arrives tails-out and flopped. You have to flop the film while rewinding it on the power rewind to get it right-side up and heads-out. Sometimes the film arrives heads-out, but you may not realize this until you have already flopped and rewound the film a few times trying to figure out what the heck is going on.

The lab assembles your workprint dailies each day into lab rolls. Lab rolls are usually approximately 1,000 feet long and comprise more than one camera roll. When the lab receives the camera rolls of film from the set each night, they do not organize the camera rolls in sequential order. Therefore, the lab rolls are rarely in camera roll-number order. This makes the syncing process more difficult.

LAB REPORTS

The lab report is a document that is produced by the lab each dailies day (see Lab Reports, Chapter 19, **The Film World**). The lab report is important for several reasons: First and foremost, it lets you know which camera rolls are on each lab roll and in which order. Secondly, it describes the "lights" at which the roll was printed. Most workprints are made with a "one light" exposure. This is why they are called "one-light prints." This means that the lab exposed the entire lab roll at one exposure setting.

The exposure setting, or "color timing," controls the density and color of the workprint. The person at the lab responsible for timing the workprint is known as the "color timer." The color timer tries to find a midrange setting that best suits the entire lab roll. This usually works just fine for film dailies. The alternative would be for the color timer at the lab to examine each scene and adjust the exposure accordingly. However, this expensive, detailed timing is reserved for certain types of reprints and final answer printing.

ORGANIZING DAILIES

Each show organizes dailies in its own way. Find out prior to principal photography in what order the director and editor wish to screen dailies. This will help determine how you organize the film each day. Some directors like to watch everything in the order it was shot. Some like to screen the dailies in scene order with master takes before closeups, etc. If multiple cameras were used, dailies can become more complicated.

ORGANIZING MULTIPLE-CAMERA DAILIES

Motion pictures can be shot with one or more cameras. Features are generally shot with one primary camera known as the "A-camera." Multiple-camera situations are frequently associated with action, stunt, or complicated shooting situations. A second camera, known as the "B-camera," is commonly used throughout principal photography for these types of situations. Multiple-camera situations alter the way dailies are synced and organized.

A protocol must be established for organizing multiple-camera material for dailies screenings. Some people like to screen B-camera material after all the A-camera material. Some people like to screen dailies in alternating setup order or alternating camera order.

The following is an example of three possible ways of organizing dailies for screening:

A-Camera Material First	Alternating Setups	Alternating Cameras
Scene/Take/Camera	Scene/Take/Camera	Scene/Take/Camera
34-1 (A-Camera)	34-1 (A-Camera)	34-1 (A-Camera)
34-2 (A-Camera)	34-2 (A-Camera)	34-1 (B-Camera)
34-4 (A-Camera)	34-4 (A-Camera)	34-2 (A-Camera)
53-3 (A-Camera)	34-1 (B-Camera)	34-2 (B-Camera)
53-5 (A-Camera)	34-2 (B-Camera)	34-4 (A-Camera)
53A-1 (A-Camera)	34-4 (B-Camera)	34-4 (B-Camera)
53A-2 (A-Camera)	53-3 (A-Camera)	53-3 (A-Camera)
53B-3 (A-Camera)	53-5 (A-Camera)	53-3 (B-Camera)
34-1 (B-Camera)	53-3 (B-Camera)	53A-1 (A-Camera)
34-2 (B-Camera)	53-5 (B-Camera)	53A-1 (B-Camera)
34-4 (B-Camera)	53A-1 (A-Camera)	53A-2 (A-Camera)
53-3 (B-Camera)	53A-2 (A-Camera)	53A-2 (B-Camera)
53-5 (B-Camera)	53A-1 (B-Camera)	53B-3 (A-Camera)
53A-1 (B-Camera)	53A-2 (B-Camera)	53B-3 (B-Camera)
53A-2 (B-Camera)	53B-3 (A-Camera)	53B-3 (A-Camera)
53B-3 (B-Camera)	53B-3 (B-Camera)	53B-3 (B-Camera)

Organizing the A-camera material first is most common since it allows the director the flexibility to screen the A-camera, the primary camera, material first with the option of continuing onto the B-camera. The studio executives prefer this method for the same reason. They often require that you indicate B-camera material on the executive screening notes so they do not have to sit through the same dailies twice.

ORGANIZING THE FILM FOR CODING

There are two main schools of thought for organizing dailies for coding:

• Example 1, "The Digital Way"– Organize the dailies into sequential daily rolls.

• Example 2, "The Film Way"– Organize individual scene material into its own daily roll with corresponding scene and ink number.

Example 1, "The Digital Way"

Features that are cut on film rather than on a digital system require that you do not mix material from different scenes on the same daily roll. This is not necessary on digital shows since the material will be eventually reorganized in the Avid.

The following is an example of a dailies breakdown for Day 28.

(DAILIES BREAKDOWN)

DATE: **Nov 7**	SHOOT DAY: **28**	VIDEO TAPE# **VT029**	
Daily Roll #123		**Daily Roll #124**	
Start Code:123-1000		Start Code:124-1000	
Scene/Take	Length	Scene/Take	Length
53-3	150'	65A-2	60'
53-5	160'	65B-3	70'
53A-1	160'	65B-4	70'
53A-2	40'	65C-1	90'
34-1	40'	65C-2	90'
34-2	30'	65C-3	90'
34-4	20'	65D-1	30'
65-1	130'	65-1(B)	140'
65-5	150'	65-5(B)	160'
65-6	100'	65-6(B)	110'
Total:	980'	Total:	910'

Day 28 (a very light day) has just less than 2,000 feet of film, which will fill two daily rolls. The dailies are organized in shooting order. Neither Sc. 53 or Sc. 34 is long enough to fill one full daily roll by itself; therefore, the first daily roll contains material from multiple scenes.

In the example above, the B-camera material is organized at the end of the second dailies roll. The director wants to see the B-camera material after all the A-camera material. (If the director wanted to see the material in shooting order with alternating cameras, Sc. 65-1, 5, 6 A-camera would be immediately followed by Sc. 65-1, 5, 6 B-camera.)

Example 2, "The Film Way"

Features that are traditionally cut on film require that you do not mix material from different scenes on the same daily roll. Some digital shows still use this protocol. The only advantage is that the scene number matches the ink number prefix. You can immediately identify a piece of film by its scene number based on the ink number. However, this process slows the syncing process considerably.

The following is an example of how dailies can be organized by scene, each in their own daily roll with corresponding ink numbers.

(DAILIES BREAKDOWN)

DATE: **Nov 7**	SHOOT DAY: **28**	VIDEO TAPE# **VT029**	
Daily Roll #123	**Daily Roll #124**		
Start Code:034-1000		Start Code:053-1000	
Scene/Take	Length	Scene/Take	Length
34-1	40'	53-3	150'
34-2	30'	53-5	160'
34-4	20'	53A-1	160'
		53A-2	40'
Total:	90'	Total:	510'

DATE: **Nov 7**	SHOOT DAY: **28**	VIDEO TAPE# **VT029**	
Daily Roll #125	**Daily Roll #126**		
Start Code:065-1000		Start Code:065-2000	
Scene/Take	Length	Scene/Take	Length
65-1	130'	65-1(B)	140'
65-5	150'	65-5(B)	160'
65-6	100'	65-6(B)	110'
65A-2	60'		
65B-3	70'		
65B-4	70'		
65C-1	90'		
65C-2	90'		
65C-3	90'		
65D-1	30'		
Total:	880'	Total:	410'

The example above is a breakdown for the same day's dailies as the previous example. Day 28 still has just less than 2,000 feet of film, which is broken down into four daily rolls rather than two daily rolls. Each scene is separated into its own daily roll. Scenes 34 and 53 are on their own daily roll. Scene 65 has too much material to fit onto one daily roll. Therefore, daily roll 125 and 126 both contain material from the same scene. The first daily roll that contains material from Sc. 65 has a starting edge-code number of 065-1000. The second daily roll that contains material from Sc. 65 starts with 065-2000. The starting ink numbers match the scene numbers rather than matching the daily roll number. The ink numbers have no correlation to the daily roll numbers.

PLANNING THE DAILIES BREAKDOWN

Once you have a protocol for organizing the film dailies for screening, you can break down the film into dailies reels as soon as it arrives each day. One way to do this is to plan it out on paper first. With the script supervisor's daily report, camera reports, and lab reports in hand, you can plan your daily roll breakdown on paper. Place as many shots on each daily roll as possible to reach 1,000 feet, a standard daily roll length. The script supervisor's daily report will tell you what was shot for the previous day, so you know what material should be arriving from the lab. The camera reports indicate the approximate length of each individual shot. These two items alone give you enough information to be able to determine which shots go on which daily roll.

The dailies breakdown applies to the picture and the track. The picture and track do not usually arrive at the same time. If you know the breakdown order for the dailies, you can break down the mag first according to how the picture will be arranged later. Most of the time, the track arrives in shooting order; however, multiple-camera situations complicate things for the track also.

B-CAM MAG

Syncing multiple-camera material creates more work for the assistant editors. Multiple cameras usually means more footage than normal. It is important that the sound transfer department receives accurate information on the sound reports in order to print multiple takes onto mag. Always check your sound transfer against the script supervisor's notes to make sure that you have all the mag before syncing dailies. The location sound mixer should have identified multiple-camera shots on the sound reports. The sound transfer department will transfer the sound twice for a two-camera setup.

ASSIGNING CODE NUMBERS

Edge code numbers, a.k.a. ink numbers, are small numbers printed onto the edge of the work picture and mag track in the editing room. They are primarily designed to keep the picture and track in sync. While cutting a movie on film, on an upright or on a flatbed, you can keep the work picture and mag in sync by aligning the corresponding ink numbers. Now that most people do not cut on film, edge code numbers are used primarily to make the conforming process easier. Edge code numbers are easier to read than key numbers. To read the key numbers on the edge of your work picture, you have to hold the film up to a light source and either read the numbers backwards or flip the film over. Additionally, the key numbers on a daily roll will not be continuous. If the lab printed take 1 and take 3 for a particular scene, the key numbers will jump between the tail of take 1 to the head of take 3, where take 2 used to be. Edge code numbers run continuously through a daily roll. This makes it so much easier to find material in a roll since you can run the film through the synchronizer and read the counter.

There are two different ways to identify and assign edge code numbers to daily rolls. In both cases, each daily roll should be assigned its own unique starting edge-code number.

Example 1, "The Digital Way"
It is not necessary to separate material from different scenes into their own daily roll on a digital show since the material will be eventually reorganized in the Avid. You can simply build the material into sequential daily rolls.

Daily Roll 123 starts at 123-1000+00 and contains material from Sc. 53, 34, and 65.
Daily Roll 124 starts at 124-1000+00 and contains material from Sc. 65.

Example 2, "The Film Way"
The other school of thought is to match the code number prefix with the scene number. Once the dailies are digitized, the code number burn-in display in the Avid will identify which scene each particular shot came from.

Daily Roll 123 starts at 034-1000+00 and only contains material from Sc. 34.
Daily Roll 124 starts at 053-1000+00 and only contains material from Sc. 53.
Daily Roll 125 starts at 065-1000+00 and only contains material from Sc. 65.

Once a daily roll is full, additional material shot for this same scene would go on the next available daily roll.

Daily Roll 126 starts at 065-2000+00 and only contains material from Sc. 65.

It is not necessary to code your dailies prior to the dailies screening or telecine. Actually, I recommend waiting until later to code the dailies to avoid dirt on your workprint. The Acmade edge-coding machine may emit dirt and tiny particles from the coding tape. It is not unusual to find white spots throughout the dailies after they have been coded.

> **TIP:** Handwrite the last edge-code number (closest to the last frame of picture) on the tail leader of each daily roll. Once the dailies have been digitized, you can visually confirm that the last code number written on the tail leader matches the Avid bin information associated with that clip.

INK NUMBER CONFORMATION

TIP: Digital shows usually have no use for the track after dailies. Therefore, you may decide not to code the track at all.

WARNING! Edge code numbers will appear in the bin as 124-1000+00 for 35mm film projects and 124-1000&00 for 16mm film projects. Check your film option setting prior to digitizing in order to avoid formatting your clips incorrectly.

ACADEMY LEADER

All daily rolls must have a uniform 12- to 20-foot head leader between the start mark and the first frame of picture. The head leader on a daily roll consists of a start mark followed by framing/focus leader for the projectionist to calibrate the projector. Edited reels must have a standard 12-foot Academy leader at the beginning. The 12-foot/8-second Academy leader is a standard in motion pictures and television. You may be familiar with the Academy countdown leader from 8 seconds with the pop at 2 seconds. The *Two-Pop* is also a standard and always occurs three feet (or two seconds) before the first frame of picture. This pop is particularly important in the later stages of the project (see Chapter **18, Sound Mix**). There should also be approximately 12 to 15 feet of leader prior to the Academy leader for projector threading proposes. There should be ample tail leader at the end of each reel with a pop two seconds (or three feet) after the last frame of picture.

When you align the Academy start mark with 0+00 on your synchronizer, the first frame of picture will be located at 12+00. The 12-foot Academy leader occurs from 0+00 until 11+15.

TELECINE

Telecine is the process of transferring film to video. Setting up telecine is one of the first and most important responsibilities on a digital show. The fate of your mental health depends on the success or failure of your telecine experience. The telecine house's accuracy in following your specifications is eminently consequential to your happiness.

A TELECINE SPECS FORM

```
FROM: Editorial                                              4/20/99
TO:   Transfer House
ATT:  Contact Person
RE:   Telecine For "The Movie"

This memo is to outline our telecine specifications.

TAPE & LOG FORMAT
1)    Telecine onto a Digital Beta master tape.
      The DigiBeta should be clean with a 1:85 mask. Do not
      include any burn-in information on the master tape. Keep
      the DigiBeta master in the vault at the lab.

2)    Make a BetaSP tape copy from the master tape.
      The BetaSP digitizing tape must be formatted as
      NDF with the hour timecode matching the daily tape #.
      Include the following burn-in information:
      Sound Timecode - Upper right
      Key Number or (Ink number) - Lower right
      Source Timecode - Lower left

3)    Provide a log file on a 3.5" floppy disk with a hard-copy
      printout.

4)    Make 2 - VHS executive copies of each dailies tape.

THE TRANSFER

1)    Please telecine in date order & scene order.

2)    Place focus/framing leader at the head of each telecine tape.

3)    The sound must be synced as follows:

      PICTURE SYNC POINT
      Use the first frame where the slate is closed but not
      blurred.

      SOUND SYNC POINT
      Sync the first modulation of sound with the sync frame on the
      picture as described above.

      The sound must be in sync. A Time Logic Controller (TLC) should
      be used. Any inaccuracies will have to be **redone** by the lab.

5)    Please FAX our office immediately regarding any negative
      problems, out-of-sync audio, or telecine problems or delays.
```

This spec sheet is for a show that does not print dailies. Therefore, the telecine house is responsible for syncing the audio. In most cases, the editorial department syncs the picture and track before the telecine process.

Telecine specifications vary on almost every project. Take time to plan your telecine carefully with the account representative at the telecine house. Use the following checklist to ensure all bases are covered before the start of principal photography:

1) The cinematographer should talk to the telecine operator regarding telecine color timing.

2) Ask the producers and studio how many viewing copies of the dailies they would like the telecine house to make each day. You do not want to turn your editing room into a dub house.

3) Provide the telecine house with a reference tone for calibrating audio levels. Ask the location sound mixer to lay a few minutes of reference tone onto a test sound roll. The location mixer will generate a reference tone from the location sound recording device for telecine audio calibration (see Calibrating Audio, Chapter 8).

4) Confirm what type of equipment the location sound mixer will use. Find out what rate (speed) and frequency the audio will be recorded at, and relay all this information to the telecine house.

REMEMBER! It is extremely important to check that the telecine is being transferred correctly (see Checking The Numbers, Chapter 8).

Direct-To-Disk

Direct-to-disk is a fairly new telecine option that provides you with a portable media drive containing your pre-digitized dailies. Usually, the telecine house transfers your film to a DigiBeta master tape. From this master tape, they make a BetaSP or 3/4-inch video tape for digitizing, and provide you with a floppy disk containing a Felx file or ALE file each day. Direct-to-disk eliminates the digitizing process in the editing room. Instead, the digitizing occurs at the telecine house immediately following the telecine transfer. Once the film has been transferred onto the DigiBeta master tape, the ALE or log file is taken to an Avid station, where a bin is created and digitized, at your specified resolution, from the digital master tape.

There are several advantages in using direct-to-disk. The most evident is the elimination of the digitizing process. The editing room is provided with a portable media drive, such as an R-Mag, which is used to transport the media from the telecine house to your Avid. In the editing room, the pre-digitized media is copied from the portable media drive onto your permanent media-storage drives each day. This process of copying the media files on the Finder level is much faster than manually digitizing the entire day's dailies. There is also no image quality loss, after compression, between the digital master tape and your media with direct-to-disk since it eliminates the intermediate analog tape step. Another valuable advantage of this process is that the audio remains 100% digital at all times, especially if the location sound mixer uses a DAT on the set. The audio never enters the analog domain.

For more information on direct-to-disk, contact D.E.S. in North Hollywood, CA, at (818) 508-8200.

CODEBOOK DATABASE

With every frame of film comes an abundance of important information that must be tracked and maintained by each cutting room: Ink Numbers, Key Numbers, Camera Roll Numbers, Sound Roll Numbers, Sound Timecode Numbers, Lab Roll Numbers, and Scene and Take Numbers. That's a lot of numbers. Making certain that this information is correct, complete, and up-to-date is a large part of responsibilities inherent in a digital editing room.

One of the best ways to keep track of all this information is through a computer database. Traditionally, film editing rooms recorded each shot's information in a handwritten codebook page that was generated as dailies were synced and logged. This information was compiled and stored in a master codebook. However, finding material and performing specific searches by shoot date or camera roll were time consuming and not practical.

Computer databases are designed to store large quantities of data in an easy-to-find, categorical, electronic filing cabinet. FileMaker Pro is a popular Mac- and Windows-based database program that I have been using on every film for the past five years. This flexible program is fully customizable and extremely easy to understand and operate. Hopefully you will create a film editing-room database that you can use from project to project.

In addition to being a powerful organizational tool in the editing room, databases have also become an integral part of the telecine process. Traditional handwritten codebook pages have been the only source of shot-by-shot information until computer databases came along. Now that all this information is stored in a database, you can provide the telecine house with an export, or portion, of the codebook database for telecine purposes instead of solely relying on the handwritten codebook pages. Most telecine houses are now database-friendly and able to import database information into whatever system they are using to telecine. This not only saves time and money, it is a far more accurate system.

In addition to FileMaker Pro, other database programs are available and may be provided to you by the telecine house. LogMill is a pre-configured database program that comes ready-to-use as an electronic film codebook database.

LOG MILL

LogMill is a Windows-based logging system for 35mm feature films. LogMill is a program designed to allow assistant editors to log film information into an electronic codebook that dictates to the telecine house where to place each daily roll on each tape. The program can be used with one or more laptop computers while syncing and logging dailies.

LogMill can create your ALE file before telecine has been completed. There is no need to subclip because every take is a master clip. Furthermore, if you use a LogMill-"enabled" telecine house, you will have the added advantage of importing and merging an audio timecode flex file into the LogMill database with correct sound timecode for each clip.

LogMill assigns a tape number to each daily roll and calculates the timecode in and out points for every take. The Ink Start Number and Ink End Numbers represent the position of each take within a daily roll. LogMill uses these numbers to calculate the Timecode in and out points. It can calculate End Key Numbers based on Ink Number duration for speedier logging.

LogMill can create Avid Log Exchange formatted files that will directly import into an Avid bin as well as Lightworks ODB files and Tab- or Comma-delimited text files for importation to other programs such as FileMaker Pro or Microsoft Access. It can also generate screening notes for dailies, codebook pages, and telecine logs.

LogMill does not currently support 16mm. Future releases will be 16mm compatible. LogMill is currently available on Windows 95, Windows 98 and NT. A Macintosh version is in the preliminary stages of development.

A free 30-session demo of the program and a manual is available at the LogMill website at http://www.dunktv.com/LM/Logmill.htm.

A TYPICAL DAY ON A FEATURE FILM

The following is an example of a possible editorial schedule. Most of the steps are similar between cutting rooms; however, the order may be vastly different.

24 Hours On A Feature Film

8:00 p.m.   Wrap shooting.

9:00 p.m.   The camera department sends the unprocessed negative to the lab with the camera reports. The camera reports indicate which takes the lab should print onto positive stock, a.k.a. workprint.

The location sound mixer sends the sound rolls to the sound transfer department with the sound reports. The sound reports indicate which takes the sound transfer department should transfer onto mag.

12:00 a.m.	The lab processes the negative.
3:00 a.m.	The lab prints the circle takes.
6:00 a.m.	The dailies supervisor at the lab checks the dailies. This person screens the dailies at high speed in a screening room.
7:00 a.m.	The mag is ready at the sound transfer department. They transfer the original sound from the sound roll onto mag some time before 7:00 a.m.
8:00 a.m.	The assistant editors arrive at work. An assistant editor picks up the mag from the sound transfer department on his/her way into work.
	Popping track begins. The assistant editors mark all the slates on the mag.
8:30 a.m.	The lab delivers the film to the cutting room.
	Marking picture begins. The assistant editors mark all the slates on the picture.
	They break the dailies down into 1,000-foot rolls and log the ink and key numbers for each take in the codebook.
9:00 a.m.	The digital assistant digitizes and organizes the dailies from the previous day in the Avid.
10:00 a.m.	The assistant editors sync the picture and track.
12:00 p.m.	An assistant editor inputs the information from the codebook pages into the logging database for telecine purposes.
	An assistant editor screens the dailies on the Kem to check for sync, scratches on the print, drop-out on the mag, and other technical problems.
1:30 p.m.	Send the dailies to the telecine department with the codebook database. Also send a hard copy of the codebook pages.
2:00 p.m.	The telecine department transfers the dailies to videotape.
2:30 p.m.	The executives screen the dailies from the previous day.
3:00 p.m.	An assistant editor codes the picture and track from the previous day.
4:00 p.m.	An assistant editor prepares dailies screening notes for the nightly screening.

5:00 p.m.	The Avid assistant organizes the footage and maintains the digital editing system.
6:30 p.m.	The telecine department makes viewing-copy dubs from the telecine master tape. They deliver the film and telecine to the cutting room.
7:00 p.m.	Distribute the viewing-copy dubs.
7:15 p.m.	The assistant editor takes the film dailies to the screening room and checks the screening room projectors and sound.
7:30 p.m.	Screen the dailies for the director.
8:30 p.m.	The assistant editor takes the dailies back to the cutting room.
9:00 p.m.	Wrap editorial.

CHAPTER 7
ORGANIZING YOUR PROJECT

CHAPTER OUTLINE

The key to being a great Avid editor is *organization*. More important than your technical knowledge, more consequential than your experience, more relevant than your proficiency, organization is critical to the success of the digital editing room.

The following section provides a guideline for organizing a project, a project folder, and configuring a project window.

CREATING A FEATURE PROJECT

Once the Avid is set up and running properly, one of the first things you do, after reading this book, is create a project. All of your work will be contained within a project that you create and name. You only need to create one project for each feature. The Avid can retain large amounts of information in one project, unlike its former adversary Lightworks.

REMEMBER! You can only have one project open at a time.

STEP BY STEP

1) Launch the Composer software.

2) The project entry window will soon appear. This dual-window dialog box

contains the user (that's you) selection on the left side and the project selection on the right side. Select New Project from the choices in the middle. If you do not have your own user settings, also create a new user from this window.

3) Name your project. Usually the project name is the same as the name of the movie.

4) Select Film Options from the dialog box, unless you are editing a video project.

5) Click OK and wait while the Composer window appears. An empty Project window will appear.

6) Click on the Settings button on the top of your project window to enter the Project Settings area.

7) Configure the most important settings that pertain to your entire project, the Film and General settings. Make sure you specify the film format, *35mm 16 ft. count*, in the Film settings and either *non-drop-frame* (NDF) or *drop-frame* (DF) timecode under the General settings. I have used NDF on every one of my projects.

TIP: Non-drop-frame timecode numbers are seperated by a colon (1:00:00:00). Drop-frame timecode numbers are seperated by a semicolon (1;00;00;00).

ORGANIZING THE PROJECT FOLDER

A feature project appears to exist on two levels in the Avid. Your project lives in the project Folder on the Finder level on the hard drive of your computer. It is also displayed in the Composer software as a project window. The project folder and project window are different renditions of the *same* project. Before 7.0, bins that were created in your project window on the Composer level automatically appeared in your project folder. However, the additional organizational folders in your project folder were not created automatically. Folders had to be made manually to store all the bins on the Finder level. Since Composer 7.0, everything is done through the project window. The project folder on the hard drive mirrors the organization of the project window.

CONFIGURING THE PROJECT WINDOW

The project window, a gray rectangular box on your bin monitor, displays all the bins in your project. The project window has four buttons in the header directly under the project name. Select the Bins button to display all the bins in the project. This is the way you will display the project window 99% of the time. The Settings button changes the project window to display the project settings. The Info button displays a summary of a few important global project options. I bet you can guess what the New Bin button does.

Pre Composer 7.0

Before your project begins, create some standard bins in your project. The project window below illustrates some of the bins found in most feature projects. Once you begin editing, remove the Dailies By Day bins from the project window. This simplifies the project window so the list is less cumbersome. Bins can be removed from the project window by deleting the bin. Hit the Delete key while a bin name is highlighted in the project window bin list. Later, if a bin does not appear in the project window, you can retrieve it by selecting Open from the File menu and finding the bin in the project folder.

A FEATURE PROJECT WINDOW BEFORE 7.0

THE MOVIE

Bins Settings Info

New Bin

●	**REEL 1 - 2 / DIR 1 (4/18)	16 K	DIR 1 (4/18)
●	**REEL 3 - 4 / DIR 1 (4/18)	16 K	DIR 1 (4/18)
●	**REEL 5 - 6 / DIR 1 (4/18)	16 K	DIR 1 (4/18)
●	*REEL 1 - 2 / EC 1 (2/14)	16 K	EC 1 (2/14)
●	*REEL 3 - 4 / EC 1 (2/14)	16 K	EC 1 (2/14)
●	*REEL 5 - 6 / EC 1 (2/14)	16 K	EC 1 (2/14)
●	*SC. 001	16 K	CUTS
●	*SC. 125	16 K	CUTS
●	DAILIES DAY 001	16 K	DAILIES BY DAY
●	DAILIES DAY 002	16 K	DAILIES BY DAY
●	DAILIES DAY 003	16 K	DAILIES BY DAY
●	LEADERS	16 K	MISC.
●	MUSIC	16 K	SFX / MUSIC
●	Scene 001	16 K	SCENE BINS
●	Scene 002 UNCUT	16 K	SCENE BINS
●	Scene 003	16 K	SCENE BINS
●	Scene 089	16 K	SCENE BINS
●	Scene 089 B-Neg	16 K	SCENE BINS
●	Scene 101	16 K	SCENE BINS
●	Scene 101 Reshoot	16 K	SCENE BINS
●	Scene 125 Inc.	16 K	SCENE BINS
●	SFX	16 K	SFX / MUSIC
●	TITLES	16 K	TITLES
●	WILD TRAX	16 K	WILD TRACKS

- *Dailies By Day bins* - contain all material from each day of telecine.
- *Cut Scene bins* - contain cuts in progress.
- *Scene bins* - contain all material organized by scene.
- *Reel bins* - contain entire cut reels.
- *Sound Effects bins* - contain sound effects.
- *Music bins* - contain canned and wild music.
- *Miscellaneous bin*- contains bars and tone, logos, etc.
- *B-Roll bins* - contain additional material, previously not requested.
- *Reshoot bins* - contain new material provided after principal photography.
- *Wild Track bins* - contain wild effects, wild dialogue, and wild ambiance.

A solid dot preceding the bin name represents a closed bin. A hollow dot preceding the bin name represents an open bin. The number following the bin name signifies the size of the bin. Bins that are created in your project window automatically appear un-filed in your project folder. Once you have filed a bin into the appropriate folder, the bin name in the project window will be followed by the corresponding folder's name. However, a question mark will appear following the bin name in the project window when you move a bin into a new folder on the Finder level while the project is open. The question mark will disappear once you open the bin once from the project window.

Project Folder Before 7.0

Organize your bins into appropriate folders; otherwise, your bins will be displayed un-sorted in one long, messy list.

A FEATURE PROJECT FOLDER

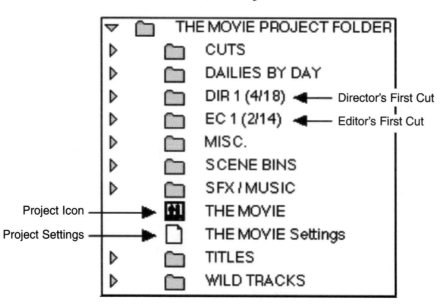

Unfortunately, this job involves a little filing. My project folder looks very much like the one pictured above. You can make as many folders as you like. My Cuts folder usually contains many folders divided by scene or version. Find a system that makes sense to you and stick with it.

REMEMBER! Bins can not be deleted through the project window before Composer 7.0. Deleting a bin from the project window only removes the bin from view. Bins can only be deleted on the Finder level.

TIP: Label extraneous bins in your project window as "trash." You can easily recognize them later in your project folder so you can throw them away.

WARNING! Try not to create bins with similar names. You may lose material if you move a bin into a project that already has a bin with that name.

WARNING! Projects, project settings, and project folders may become corrupt over time. Replace corrupt files and folders when necessary.

Project Window for Composer 7.0 and Beyond

With the introduction of Composer 7.0, project organization is much easier. The new project window adopts the same configuration you are used to with the Mac Operating System (Mac OS). The project window's hamburger menu allows you to create new folders, delete unused bins, empty the project trash, and view the naked bins outside of their folders.

A FEATURE PROJECT WINDOW AFTER 7.0

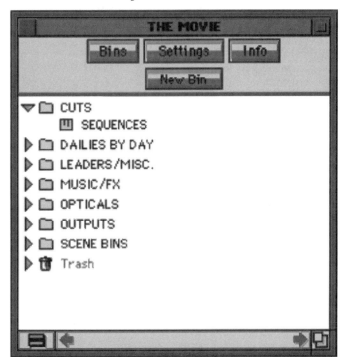

One of the most useful functions added to the project window after 7.0 is the ability to be more organized. You can now create folders, organize bins into folders, and delete bins and folders directly in the project window. There is a trash can that automatically appears at the bottom of your project window any time you try to delete a bin or folder. The items in the trash can either be placed back into the project window or removed permanently by emptying the trash.

EMPTYING THE TRASH

The Trash can allows you to permanently delete bins and folders directly within Composer without going out to the Finder level.

STEP BY STEP

1) Highlight the bin or folder you wish to delete.

2) Hit the Delete key on your keyboard. The trash can will automatically appear at the bottom of the project window, now containing the deleted bin or folder.

3) Select Empty Trash from the project window's hamburger menu. A dialog box will appear asking if you wish to delete or cancel. Once the trash has been emptied, the trash can will disappear.

Bins and folders can be dragged into the trash if they already appear in the project window. Items within the trash can not be opened.

WARNING! Any item can be removed from the trash. However, once the trash has been emptied, the item is permanently eliminated. If you accidentally trash an item, check your attic for a recent backup.

WARNING! Do not duplicate bin or folder names. You may lose material if you move a bin into a project that already has a bin with that name.

WARNING! Projects, project settings, and project folders may become corrupt over time. Replace corrupt files and folders when necessary.

DISTRIBUTING DAILIES INTO SCENE BINS

Before digitizing your dailies, create a new bin and name it "Dailies Day 01." Digitize all the material from the first day of telecine into this bin. You may have more than one tape from each day. A separate log file should accompany each tape. After all the material has been digitized into the daily bin, you are now ready to distribute the footage into scene bins. Do not move, delete, or edit using any clips in your dailies bins. The dailies bin should contain unaltered original master clips.

STEP BY STEP

1) Create a bin named Temp Scene bin.

2) Select all clips in the dailies bin and copy them into the temporary bin. Drag the clips while depressing the Option key.

3) Close the Dailies Day 01 bin.

4) Set the Temp bin to Text view.

5) Sort the bin by clip name.

6) Select Center Pan from the Clip menu to direct mono audio to play through the left and right speakers. There is also a global center pan feature in the Audio settings.

7) Switch the bin view back to Frame view.

8) Select Fill Sorted from the bin's hamburger menu.

9) Set up a representative frame for every clip in the bin (see Setting Representative Frames below).

10) Distribute all the material from the Temp bin into the appropriate scene bins. Once all the clips have been placed in the proper bins, your Temp bin should be empty. You will be sure that all the dailies material has been distributed when nothing is left in the Temp bin. Meanwhile, all the original master clips still exist in the dailies bin.

11) Arrange the clips in the scene bins in a orderly manner. This procedure varies from editor to editor, day to day. It is a very personal choice. The material should be displayed in such a manner that everything is easy to find.

TIP: While in Text view, sort the clips by name. Switch to Film view and fill the clips in order by selecting Fill Sorted from the bin hamburger menu. You can not sort the clips in a bin while in Frame view.

SETTING REPRESENTATIVE FRAMES

Following the digitizing process, you should set representative frames for all your clips. It is easier to edit using clips preset with representative frames. Representative frames are used to illustrate the essential content of each clip. The Avid default for each clip's representative frame is the first frame of the shot. This usually provides you with a bin full of small images of slates or punch frames.

There are two ways to set representative frames for the clips in your bin.

OPTION ONE - STEP BY STEP

1) While in Frame view, select a clip in the bin.

2) Using the 1, 2, 3, 4 buttons on the keyboard, advance or reverse the clip frame-by-frame or by eight frames and find the frame that best represents the contents of the clip.

1 key = reverse 8 frames
2 key = advance 8 frames
3 key = reverse 1 frame
4 key = advance 1 frame

(The 1 and 2 keys count for ten frames in a video project.)

When you are done, the bin remembers the representative frame and will display it each time you open the bin.

REMEMBER! A bin must be activated before accessing a clip within it. Click anywhere in a bin to activate it. A bin header turns purple when activated. Even if a clip appears highlighted in a bin in which the header is not purple, the clip is not activated.

OPTION TWO - STEP BY STEP

1) In either Frame or Text view, load the clip into the source monitor.

2) Scroll through the clip and find one frame that best illustrates the entire shot.

3) Mark-in on that frame.

4) Highlight the clip in the bin and hit Q on the keyboard. Notice that the Q key doubles as the Goto In-Point key.

The Q causes the bin to automatically display the frame at the point of the in-mark. For efficiency, set an in-mark for all the clips in the bin. Highlight all the clips in the bin and click Q on the keyboard. All the clips will represent the frame at the point of the in-mark.

CUSTOM COLOR BIN BACKGROUNDS

The bin background palette is one of my favorite features. I could spend hours designing bin backgrounds. The Composer default color for bin backgrounds is gray. You can color-code bins for organizational purposes or just for aesthetics. The bin Font and the bin Background settings can be found under the Edit menu.

COLOR BIN BACKGROUNDS

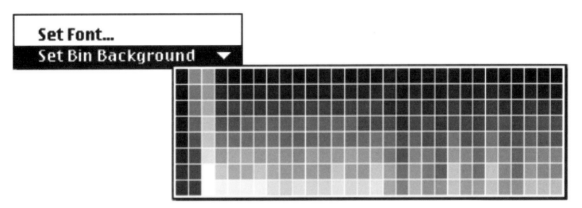

TIP: Hold the Option key when you select Set Bin Background from the Edit menu. In some Composer versions, this will display the color picker rather than the color palette.

CHAPTER OUTLINE

Digitizing is the process of inputting media into a digital editing system. Media are the audio and video components that digital systems play.

In the feature world, dailies usually are printed onto film before the telecine process. Many low-budget projects save money by telecining directly from negative. However, this shortcut comes with its fair share of problems. For instance, the telecine house handles your negative, which scratches easily, rather than the workprint. Additionally, it is harder to check focus from a videotape than a film print. Whichever method you choose, your telecine material will most likely be delivered on a videotape format. Some telecine houses have the ability to telecine directly onto media drives (see Direct-To-Disk, Chapter 6). Digital editing systems can only digitize from a videotape format. Currently, Avid systems do not have the ability to digitize directly from film or negative.

Your dailies tapes should arrive from the telecine house clearly labeled and each with a different tape-identification number. The accompanying log file disk should have a corresponding dailies tape number.

Tape 1, labeled as VT 001, starts at 01:00:00:00.
Tape 10, labeled as VT 010, starts at 10:00:00:00.
Tape 20, labeled as VT 020, starts at 20:00:00:00.
Tape 21, labeled as VT 021, starts at 21:00:00:00.

This chapter describes a typical daily digitizing routine for a feature film.

DIGITIZING FEATURE DAILIES, STEP BY STEP

STEP BY STEP

- STEP # 1 Convert the log files into ALE files
- STEP # 2 Create a new dailies bin
- STEP # 3 Import the ALE file into the new dailies bin
- STEP # 4 Modify the master clips
- STEP # 5 Calibration
- STEP # 6 Batch digitizing
- STEP # 7 Checking your work

• STEP # 1. Convert the log files into ALE files.

The first step in digitizing film dailies is converting the log files. Log files are documents created by the telecine house during the telecine process. These "Logs" are text information that may include scene and take numbers, key numbers, edge code numbers, sound roll and camera roll numbers, source timecode, tape number, and pull-in frame information. Log files come in different types, such as Flex, Evertz, Key Logs (a.k.a. FTL), usually on a 3.5-inch PC-formatted disk.

1) At the beginning of your project, create a folder on your desktop and name it Log Files. Store one copy of each Log and ALE file in this folder (see Avid Log Exchange below).

2) Insert the floppy from the telecine house and make a copy of the log file into your Log Files folder. Always work with your copy of the log file rather than using

the original to prevent any damage to the original file. Eject the floppy and store it in a disk box for safe keeping. You probably will not need to use the disk again unless your copy of the log file becomes corrupt.

3) Convert the log file into an ALE file. Keep both the log file and the new ALE file in the Log Files folder.

AVID LOG EXCHANGE is a software program that converts the logs you receive from the telecine house into Avid Log Exchange files (a.k.a. ALE files). You can't import log files, Flex or Evertz, etc., into Composer. You must first convert these files into ALE files.

Converting Log Files

STEP BY STEP

(STANDARD WAY)
1) Open the ALE application program.

2) Select the type of log file you want to convert. If you are not sure what type of log file you have, select Automatic and ALE will determine the type of log file you are using.

3) Select Convert, and find the log you want to translate.

(MY WAY)
1) Open the ALE application program.

2) Select Automatic for the type of log file you want to convert. This allows ALE to automatically recognize the type of log file. The Clean function eliminates overlapping timecode numbers; I don't use this unnecessary function.

3) Quit the application. Your ALE settings are now saved.

4) Drag the log file directly onto the ALE icon. The log file will magically translate into an ALE file. You never need to open ALE again.

• **STEP # 2. Create a new dailies bin.**

For each day of the shoot, create a new dailies bin in your project. Digitize all the material from one day of dailies into its own dailies bin. On the first day of the shoot, name the bin Dailies Day 01. It is important to retain an unaltered copy of the original master clips in your dailies bin (see Organizing Your Project, Chapter 6).

In your project folder on the desktop level, create a new folder and name it Dailies By Day. This folder will contain all the Dailies By Day bins.

• STEP # 3. Import the ALE file into the new dailies bin.

The new dailies bin you create will be empty until you import the converted log file. This process takes a few minutes.

STEP BY STEP

    1) Highlight the dailies bin and select Import from the File menu.

    2) Make sure the file type is set to Shot Log.

    3) Locate the logs file folder on the desktop and select the appropriate ALE file.

    4) Add this file to the bin and select Done (unconverted log files will not import).

Select files to import

```
┌───────────────────┐                  ⊂⊃ TONY
│ 🗀 VT 046  ▼        │
├───────────────────┬─┐   ┌ ─ ─ ─ ─ ─ ─ ─ ┐ ─ ─ ─ ┐
│ ▦ HF046.ALE       │⇧│   │    Eject      │       ▶
│                   ├─┤   └ ─ ─ ─ ─ ─ ─ ─ ┘
│                   │ │   ┌───────────────┐
│                   │ │   │   Desktop     │
│                   │ │   └───────────────┘
│                   │ │   ┌───────────────┐
│                   │ │   │     Add       │
│                   ├─┤   └───────────────┘
│                   │⇩│   ┌───────────────┐
└───────────────────┴─┘   │   Add All     │
                          └───────────────┘
 File Type ┌─────────────┐┌───────────────┐    ┌─┐ Com
           │  Shot Log   ││   Remove      │    └─┘ auto
           └─────────────┘└───────────────┘
                          ┌───────────────┐
                          │  Remove All   │
                          └───────────────┘
```

    5) Check the accuracy of the bin contents against the hard copy of the log file from the telecine house.

    TIP: Hold the Option key down when you select Import from the file menu. This will display all files, regardless of type, in the import dialog box.

    TIP: Telecine houses that offer Direct-to-Disk will provide you will a pre-made bin in addition to a log file.

• STEP # 4. Modify the master clips.

The log files you import into your dailies bin may not contain the appropriate information you require. Hopefully, the telecine house has created accurate log files. However, most telecine houses make certain assumptions about your project that you should verify before digitizing.

The telecine house assumes you want to digitize both audio channels from the source tape. The log file they provided will probably indicate both audio channels. It is not necessary to digitize two tracks of audio for most feature projects. Your dialogue was probably recorded in mono on the set. Therefore, you only need to digitize one track of audio for each clip. Two tracks of the same thing does not make it sound better, it just makes it louder.

You may have to modify all the clips imported from the log file as a course of normal procedure. Always check the sound reports before modifying any clips. The location sound mixer may have recorded some takes with split channels. This would provide you with two different audio channels on your source tape. You should digitize only one audio channel for any mono recordings and both audio channels for any stereo or split-channel recordings. The sound report should indicate when split channels have been used.

The digitizing tool examines the log information to determine which audio channels to digitize. Therefore, it is necessary to modify the dual-audio-channel master clips in the bin prior to digitizing.

Modifying Clips

STEP BY STEP

1) Set the bin headings to display the clip names and tracks.

2) Select all the master clips that include both audio channels and one video channel (V1, A1, and A2).

3) Under the Clip menu, select Modify then Set Tracks. Deselect all but V1 and A1. Wild tracks should be modified with A1 only.

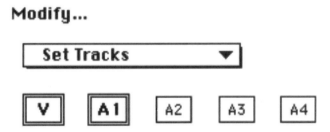

TIP: MOS shots should have already been set to digitize only V1 by the telecine house. Make sure you are not digitizing audio for MOS shots.

TIP: Wild tracks should be set to digitize only A1. It is not necessary to digitize the video channel for wild track clips. Wild tracks are usually recorded in mono. However, if the sound was recorded in stereo, digitize both audio channels.

TIP: You cannot directly modify the number of audio tracks for a subclip. However, if you unlink and modify the number of audio tracks for a master clip, the associated subclip(s) will default to the master clip.

Unlinking

Modifying a clip may be necessary after digitizing. Whether or not you forgot to modify the clip or you realized that the sound reports were incorrect and the recording was done in stereo, you can modify and redigitize the clip.

A digitized clip will permit several modifications, such as changing the clip name or sound timecode numbers. However, a digitized clip can not be modified as easily as a hollow clip. A digitized clip will *not* permit certain modifications, such as modifying the tracks or starting timecode.

If you have digitized a clip in error and need to make a modification due to incorrect log information or track assignment, you must delete the media associated with the clip before you can modify it. However, even after you have deleted the associated media, the Avid will still prevent you from modifying the clip. The Avid has latent emotional attachments to the media that was once there—it will not give up without a fight. Therefore, in addition to deleting the media, you will have to *unlink* the clip, freeing it to be modified.

Unlinking eliminates all current and latent attachments between a clip and its associated media. Digitized clips can be unlinked and relinked from their associated media. Try it at work; it really scares the editor.

STEP BY STEP

   1) Highlight a clip in a bin.

   2) Hold down the Shift and Control keys and select Unlink from the Clip menu.

• STEP # 5. Calibration.

Calibration is one of the most important elements in digitizing your dailies. It is a process you will hopefully only do once per tape. You will be looking and listening to these images for a long time and they should be good. All editors have their own personal preferences for calibrating audio and video. However, to be able to develop your own system, you first must understand the standard way to calibrate.

There are two areas of calibration in all analog tape formats, audio and video. Audio calibration controls the audio amplitude levels. Video calibration controls the luminance and chroma levels. The Composer software is equipped with video input control features. The Composer's audio-input level controls are primarily external and not found in the software.

"Bars and Tone"

All telecine dailies should contain bars and tone at the beginning of each tape. "Bars and Tone" is a standard image and tone used to calibrate audio and video levels for all video formats. Your digitizing tool is equipped with video calibration tools, Waveform and Vectorscope, and an audio level meter, Audio Tool.

Audio

It is important to digitize clean and strong audio into your system since your digitized audio may be eventually used as your temp audio for previews. The Avid does not compress audio; therefore, no significant quality is lost during the digitizing process for audio.

CALIBRATING AUDIO

STEP BY STEP

1) Open the Audio Tool while in capture mode.

Changing the audio levels in the Audio Tool does not affect the actual audio input levels. The Audio Tool controls the volume levels in the Avid.

2) Play the bars and tone at the head of your source tape. The VU meter on the deck should be registering "0" for tone. If the audio on your source tape is too high or too low, adjust the deck output through your mixing board.

3) Adjust the deck output levels on the mixer so that the tone falls between -11 dB and -15 dB on the Audio Tool.

If you do not have a mixer attached to your system, you can adjust audio input levels by inserting a tiny screwdriver into the input level trim on the Pro Tools audio interface and turning the tiny screw clockwise. However, these adjustments are crude and limited. This is why it is crucial that the telecine house transfer audio at the appropriate levels.

AUDIO TOOL

TECHNICAL JUNK: Analog audio meters are not on a 1:1 corresponding scale with digital audio meters. Where "0" on an analog VU meter may be an acceptable level for audio, in the digital world "0" signifies the top of the scale where clipping occurs (a.k.a. distortion in the analog world). The corresponding equivalent for analog "0" lies between -11dB and -15dB on a digital audio meter.

CALIBRATING VIDEO

Calibrating video levels is slightly more difficult than audio. It is important to digitize high-quality video into your system since you will be looking at these images for a long time.

The Avid compresses video. Therefore, your digitized image will not look as good as the original. There are many levels of compression, called *resolution* or Avid Video Resolution (AVR), that determine the quality of the digitized image. By calibrating video correctly, everything in the frame should be visible (see Selecting a Resolution, Chapter 8).

"Bars" is a standard image used to calibrate video levels for all video formats. Your digitizing tool is equipped with two video-calibration devices, the Waveform and Vectorscope. The Waveform tool controls the video luminance through two settings, setup and gain. The Vectorscope tool controls the video chroma through two settings, hue and saturation.

Calibrating Video Before Digitizing

STEP BY STEP

1) Open the Waveform and Vetorscope tools while in the capture mode.

2) Play the bars and tone at the head of your source tape.

3) Adjust the Waveform and Vectorscope levels. The Line shuttle button adjusts the Video Calibration tool to recognize either the luminance or chroma levels on the video. Slide the button until it reveals the twin towers for calibrating luminance. Slide the line button to the right until the triangular pattern appears in the Vetorscope monitor for calibrating chroma levels.

WAVEFORM MONITOR   VECTORSCOPE

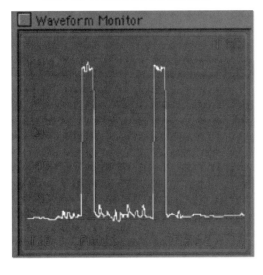 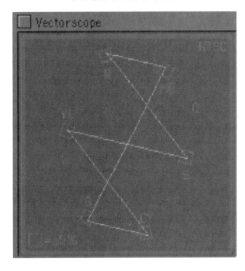

Waveform Monitor
The Waveform displays the video luminance (brightness). The object of this game is to make the white lines representing towers reach close to the 100 IRE level while the bottom white lines, the peaks and valleys, sit on the dotted line.

Vectorscope
The Vectorscope displays the hue and saturation (color levels). The object of this game is to position the corners of the triangles inside the boxes. The R box (red), YL box (yellow), G box (Green), CY box (Cyan), B box (Blue) and MG box (Magenta) represent the colors of the Vectorscope spectrum.

TIP: Try to place the red-box triangle as close to the center of the R box. Red is the predominant color found in *all* skin tones. Your actors will look better if the red hue is set properly (assuming your actors are human).

Composite or Component

There are two types of video signals, composite and component. A singular stream of video that contains color and luminance information is a composite signal. Consumer video equipment uses a composite video signal. A set of divided color and luminance streams of information that together comprise a single high-quality video signal is a component signal. Some professional video equipment has component video inputs and outputs. If your Avid is inputting a component video signal, it may not be necessary to calibrate for chroma.

Saving Video Tool Settings

Once you have calibrated the video input levels, save these settings. The video input settings are saved by tape name. Each time you digitize from a pre-calibrated tape, the digitizing tool will default to your previously saved video settings.

SAVE YOUR TAPE SETTINGS

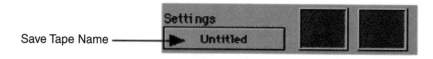

Save Tape Name ——— Settings / Untitled

TIP: Digitize 30 seconds of bars and tone into a miscellaneous bin. You can use this clip later to calibrate outputs.

BATCH DIGITIZING

• **STEP # 6.** Batch digitizing.

Batch digitizing is the Avid's auto-pilot mode for digitizing. It is the process of automatically digitizing media from previously logged clips. The process does not necessarily refer to a group or batch of anything. Even if you are just auto-digitizing one clip, setting the Avid to automatically digitize an empty clip is known as batch digitizing. Whether you have created clips through the logging tool in capture mode or imported clips from a flex file, you can set the Avid to automatically digitize hollow clips.

Before digitizing, you have to make a few decisions about your project. This is the point when you have to select a destination drive, a sample rate, and a resolution.

Selecting a Destination Drive

Organizing your media will save you time and effort in the future. Develop a plan for assigning dailies to particular destination media drives. Store all the media from one day of dailies on the same media drive and keep a record of what material is stored on each media drive. If you ever lose a drive, you will be able to immediately determine what material is missing from your project, making it easier to replace it.

One theory suggests that storing the audio and video portions of the media associated with a clip in different media drives will enable the system to access the media more efficiently. This is necessary for certain high-quality two-field resolutions, but I have not experienced the need to put this theory into practice on a feature project.

> **TIP:** Notice that the media files on the media drives have long, meaningless identification numbers as their names. Part of the media file name consists of the source-tape number. If you modify log files before digitizing to represent not only the tape number but also the appropriate scene number, this information will appear as the first part of the media file's name.

MEDIA FILE

110v008_V01.AEE45917_AECB1ECB

This piece of media comes from scene 110 on dailies tape 008.

Sample Rate

The Avid can input at two different sample rates, 44.1kHz or 48kHz. The sample rate 44.1kHz is generally used for feature projects and is comparable to CD quality. It is perfectly adequate for most audio. The wider frequency band, 48kHz, accommodates broader audio frequencies like the ones found on some high-quality DAT tapes, but it also utilizes more media drive space. Ask your sound editors if they have a sample rate preference before you start a show.

Selecting a Resolution

Before starting an Avid project, you must decide at what AVR (Avid Video Resolution) you would like to digitize your show. There are several resolutions to pick from (see AVR list). The better-quality resolutions utilize more storage space. A lower or more fragmented resolution, such as AVR 1, compresses the most footage per gigabyte and therefore maximizes your drive capacity by sacrificing picture quality.

AVR LIST

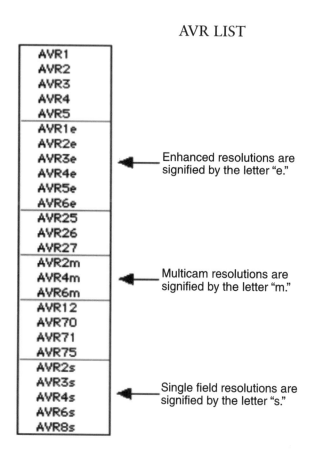

ENHANCEMENT BOARD (E-Board) - Some older systems come with an enhancement board. This device improves the compression ratio and actually softens the jagged edges of the pixels, providing better picture quality. A system using an enhancement board contains AVR levels signified by "e" after the name, e.g., AVR3e.

There is a simple formula to determine your resolution. The difficult part is estimating the final total footage count. First, find out how much footage is budgeted for your show. The footage, in hours, divided into the total storage capacity of your media drives at a certain AVR will let you know if you have enough gigs. The AVR level will determine the number of minutes per gigabyte.

The Storage Calculator helps determine your media drive needs. Ask your system provider to install this handy feature on your system. The calculator is self-explanatory and easy to use. Just enter the information in the empty boxes for an immediate footage-per-gigabyte calculation.

STORAGE CALCULATOR

WARNING! Digitize at the same AVR for your entire project when using any software versions prior to 6.0. Different resolutions cannot be cut together in the same sequence on the older software versions. Since version 6.0, you can now combine any combination of single-field resolutions and any combination of two-field resolutions (but not single-field with two-field).

REMEMBER! In digital editing, resolution refers only to the picture quality. Audio quality is not measured in resolutions. The Avid does not compress audio.

TIP: During the digitizing process, you will be creating separate media files. Audio and video files are not necessarily married once they enter a digital editing system. Audio and video media files may be stored together or separately, but some two-field resolutions require that you store the audio and video files separately.

Batch Digitizing

Once you have selected a destination drive, a sample rate, and a resolution, you are now ready to batch digitize.

STEP BY STEP

1) Highlight the hollow clip(s) in the bin.

2) Select Batch Digitize from the Clip menu.

TIP: You can leave the Avid unattended while you digitize. However, the Avid will stop digitizing if there are any problems, such as a break in timecode, unless you change the digitize setting to allow the system to temporarily ignore the problem and move on. The system will complete digitizing all clips except where a problem has occurred. A dialog box will indicate whether or not the batch digitizing process was Complete or Incomplete. You can check the console for error messages pertaining to the problem clips.

Batch Digitize Settings (Current)
☒ Log errors to the console and continue digitizing.

REMEMBER! Any material, such as dailies, that has gone through the telecine process must be digitized with the pulldown set to x 0.99. Any material, such as music from a CD or audio from a DAT, should be digitized with the pulldown set to x 1.00 (see How Does It Work?, Chapter 1).

Digitizing Manually

You can manually digitize material into the Avid by selecting the big red button in the digitizing tool.

BIG RED BUTTON

Just remember, while digitizing 24-fps dailies on the fly, always start digitizing on an "A" frame. The "film-to-tape" conversion works properly if the Avid pulls the "A" frame in first. Make sure the clip's last digit in the starting timecode number ends with a 0 or a 5. Since 3-2 pulldown works in cycles of four (A, B, C, and D), the first frame and the fifth frame are both "A" frames (all reputable telecine houses follow this protocol). Digitizing by starting on a "B," "C," or "D" frame will cause your image to strobe (see Changing The Pull-In Frame in step #7 below).

REMEMBER! Mixing AVRs within a sequence is okay since Composer version 6.0.

• STEP # 7. Check Your Work

It is extremely important to check your work after digitizing. It is better to find a discrepancy sooner than later. Make a checklist and follow it every time you bring new media into the system.

CHECKLIST FOR DIGITIZING

1) Check the pulldown rate.

All telecine dailies should be digitized at "x 0.99." All non-telecine material should be digitized at "x 1.00."

2) Center pan all the clips.

Mono audio is panned either left or right depending on which channel has audio. By selecting All Tracks Centered from the Audio Settings box, all mono audio will be played through both the left and the right channels for your entire project.

3) Check for strobing media.

Make sure all clips start on an "A" frame. Clips digitized starting with a "B," "C," or "D" frame will strobe when played back. Some scenes are harder than others to determine whether or not strobing has occurred. Look at the burn-in information to see if the last digit of the key number blurs as you play the clip frame-by-frame. A blurred digit indicates a wrong pull-in frame (see How Does It Work?, Chapter 1). Occasionally a clip may strobe even though the log file indicates an "A" frame at the start. This occurs when the telecine house does not start on an "A" frame but likes to pretend it did. This scenario has two solutions: You could ask the telecine house to re-telecine the material or you could modify the master clip as follows:

Changing the Pull-In Frame

STEP BY STEP

    a) Delete the strobing media.
    b) Select Modify from the Clip menu.
    c) Select Set Pull-in from the menu.
    d) Change the pull-in frame to "B."
    e) Re-digitize the master clip.

If the strobing recurs, try changing the pull-in frame to "C" or "D." It's potluck.

REMEMBER! Set the last digit in the starting timecode number to a 5 or 0 digit when digitizing on the fly (see Digitizing Manually in the previous section).

4) Play back each clip.

It is always a good idea to watch new clips all the way through after digitizing. This eliminates the possibility of a problem going undetected. I don't like those types of surprises and neither do most editors.

5) Confirm that the burn-in information matches the logs and codebook.

Attention to detail is important. The information stored in a digital editing system must be checked and double-checked. Remember that your cut lists are made from the bin information. Bin information originates from log files. Log files are either created entirely by the telecine house or in conjunction with the editing room via a computer database. No matter how the information gets into the Avid, I guarantee that at least one number in all those thousands of numbers will be wrong. It's your job to find the discrepancies and fix them.

Checking the Numbers

STEP BY STEP

1) Set the bin to display the following headings: Clip Name, Scene, Take, Pull-in, Source Timecode Start, KN Start, Ink Start, and Sound Timecode Start. Bin headings can be customized by selecting Headings from the bin's hamburger menu. Save the set of headings in a bin display.

2) Set the source monitor readout to display the two most important sets of numbers, e.g., key or ink numbers and sound timecode.

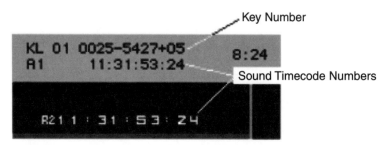

3) Check the head and tail of each clip. Make sure the bin information matches the burn-in. If a discrepancy exists, track the information back to the source and find the problem. Key numbers can be checked against your workprint. Sound timecode numbers may be checked by playing your mag on a flatbed equipped with a sound timecode reader.

REMEMBER! Sound timecode numbers do not move for MOS clips.

TIP: Sometimes sound timecode numbers match at the head of a clip but do not match at the tail of a clip. This is a common occurrence. There are two simple explanations: 1) The original sound-roll timecode for that clip is not continuous from the beginning of the clip. The location sound mixer may have paused or started the sound roll late. 2) Another possibility may be that the sound timecode burn-in has not caught up with the picture. In either case, the telecine operator probably looked at the first sound timecode number and entered this number as the first correct starting sound timecode number. However, since the sound timecode had not reached speed or does not continue uninterrupted, the number they entered will not match the bin information.

SOLUTION: Stop at a point in the clip where the burn-in sound timecode numbers continue uninterrupted. Calculate the duration back to the head of the clip and subtract this number from the sound timecode number at your current position. Correct the bin information to match the burn-in.

HOW TO DIGITIZE FROM JUST ABOUT ANYTHING

The Avid can digitize from just about any audio or video format you can imagine. I often load 8mm or VHS home movies into the system and edit fun pieces for my family. There are only two technical requirements for imputing various audio or video formats into the Avid. First, the source device must have the ability to output. Most consumer video cameras and decks have audio and video RCA output jacks. Most consumer audio equipment is also equipped with RCA connections. It really does not matter what format of connector you have on the source device because there are many adapters that convert RCA to BNC and XLR. The second technical requirement is that no matter what the source is, you have to enter the Avid through the designated BNC and XLR connections. The Avid inputs audio through XLR connectors and video through a BNC connector. A RCA to BNC adapter can easily route a consumer video signal from a camcorder into the Avid.

The digitize settings have options that will prevent you from digitizing from a non-timecoded source or a non-Avid-controlled deck. These options have to be deactivated before you can digitize from a non-timecoded format.

Digitizing from a Source Without Timecode

The Avid requires timecode information from your sources unless you change the default Digitize Setting in the project. Under the Digitize Settings, de-select Always digitize the timecode from the source. Also deselect Always digitize from an Avid controlled deck if you are digitizing from any deck that is not directly controlled by the Avid. If you are in capture mode and would like to change these setting, use keystroke ⌘ – = to open the Digitize Settings window.

Digitize Settings (Current)

☐ Always display incoming video in the Edit monitor.
→ ☐ Always digitize the timecode from the source.
→ ☐ Always digitize from an Avid controlled deck.
☐ Ask before discarding a canceled clip.
☐ Capture a single video frame only.
☐ Digitize across timecode breaks.

STEP BY STEP

1) In capture mode, click the small icon that vaguely resembles a video deck to digitize from a non-Avid-controlled deck. The Source Name? window will appear asking you to select a source.

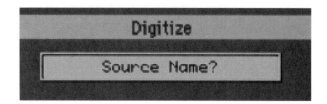

2) Label your source. If you are digitizing from a compact disc, name the source "CD." The same applies for VHS, Hi8, 8mm, tape without timecode, audio cassettes, and DAT without timecode.

3) Deselect the TC button next to the track buttons.

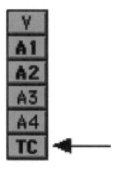

WARNING! Any material digitized into the Avid without timecode *cannot* be re-batch digitized. If the media is deleted from these non-timecoded sources, you must redigitize from scratch and re-cut the material manually. To avoid this problem, copy all your non-timecoded material onto a timecoded tape. If you are working with music from CDs, record your music onto a timecoded tape source and digitize from this tape. If your media drives ever crash, you will be able to batch-digitize from your timecoded tape.

CAPTURE MODE TROUBLESHOOTING

PROBLEM: The Avid is displaying a black bar with dancing white spots across the record monitor during digitizing.
SOLUTION: This bar is the vertical interval timecode information from your tape. Your deck is not in perfect video sync with the Avid. This is not a sound-sync problem. Eject the source tape and press the record tab. The record tab is the small plastic button, usually red, that prevents you from recording onto a tape. If this problem continues, check the cable connections. Also check that the black burst generator is working properly.

PROBLEM: The deck is not responding to the Avid commands.
SOLUTION: First check that the deck is turned on. Make sure the deck is set to Remote, not Local.

PROBLEM: The Avid says No Driver in digitize mode. The Avid is not recognizing that a deck is attached to the system.
SOLUTION: Under the Tools menu, select Console and type "check decks" in the console window. Some Composer versions have a handy Check Decks function under the Deck Selection menu in the digitizing tool. Check your connections between the deck and the computer. If the deck still does not come online, try restarting the Avid with the deck turned on.

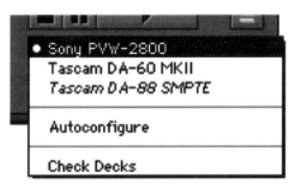

PROBLEM: In capture mode, the deck is getting lost when passing a break in timecode as it prerolls.
SOLUTION: If your mark-in point is too close to a break in timecode on your source tape, the Avid will not be able to digitize the material. The deck will preroll and get lost when passing a break in timecode. You can either change the preroll time (e.g., from 5 sec. to 3 sec.) or move your in-mark later so the Avid has more space to preroll.

The Preroll setting is in your project under Deck. If you have logged your clips and begun to batch digitize, the Avid will perform this task in an autopilot mode unless there is a timecode break. If you leave the room, the Avid may not complete the batch until you resolve the problem.

WARNING! The Avid has trouble digitizing from tapes longer than 60 minutes. The system is programmed to recognize timecoded tape lengths of one hour or less. If your tape is longer than one hour, the Avid may think you have two source tapes rather than one.

CHAPTER 9
SCSI MEDIA SHARE

CHAPTER OUTLINE

Hardware
Software
Setting Up MSScanner
Moving Material

The SCSI Media Share system is designed to allow multiple Avids to access the same media simultaneously. The entire Media Share system, or "media scare" as my friend Dale Jones calls it, is simple and extremely easy to understand and operate. The Media Share "box" and the MSScanner software are the only two additional components needed to add to an existing Avid(s) in order to transform it into a SCSI Media Share system.

HARDWARE

MEDIA SHARE BOX
The Media Share box is a small device that connects in the SCSI chain between the media drives and the Avid. The media drives are looped together in a chain that connects to the Media Share box that each Avid is connected to. The box acts like a traffic cop in a busy intersection directing the flow of media to the Avids.

SOFTWARE

MSSCANNER
Multiple Avids may not write to the same drive at the same time. Multiple access to media is on a "read only" basis. Any attempt to simultaneously write to a drive from multiple workstations will result in a crash. The software MSScanner is designed to protect your drives from this event. MSScanner administrates write privileges to your Avids. This software runs in conjunction with Film/Media Composer. Each Avid on a Media Share system should keep MSScanner running during operation.

SETTING UP MSSCANNER

Setting up MSScanner is a fairly simple process, although the program has to be customized to your particular systems. This entails assigning and restricting access privileges to the drives.

STEP BY STEP

1) One very small partition on your drives must be devoted to MSScanner and should be labeled with the exact name "Media Share". The MSScanner preferences file is stored on this partition.

2) Open the MSScanner software.

3) Designate the assistant's Avid as the administrating system and the Editor's Avid as an additional system. Identify each Avid by the name in the Users & Groups setting in the Control Panel.

4) Select Administrate from the ScanVolume menu.

MEDIA SHARE ADMINISTRATOR

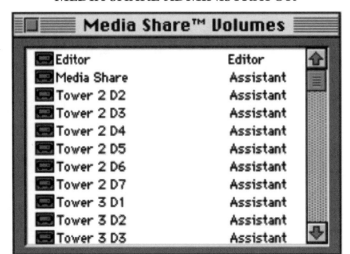

5) The Media Share Administrator Box will open. Assign access privileges by placing your computer's name next to all the drives that you should have access to. Remember, the only media created on the editor's system should come from creating dissolves and other effects. Therefore, the editor only needs access to one partition on which to render effects. The assistant's system should have access privileges to all the remaining drives.

MEDIA SHARE ACCESS PREFERENCES

```
 Volume Name      Total         Free   Locked
 -----------      -----         ----   ------

 Tower 3 D1     477.4 MB      3.2 GB      No
 Tower 3 D2     477.4 MB      2.9 GB      No
 Tower 3 D3     477.4 MB      2.5 GB      No
 Tower 3 D4     477.4 MB      1.8 GB      No
 Tower 3 D6     477.4 MB      2.5 GB      No
 Tower 3 D7     477.4 MB      3.2 GB      No
 Tower 2 D2     477.4 MB    466.6 MB      No
 Tower 2 D3     585.0 MB    582.7 MB      No
      Editor      3.9 GB      3.9 GB     Yes
Media Share      19.4 MB     19.0 MB      No
 Tower 2 D4     477.4 MB      3.6 GB      No
 Tower 2 D5     477.4 MB    474.7 MB      No
 Tower 2 D6     477.4 MB    474.7 MB      No
 Tower 2 D7     477.4 MB    474.2 MB      No
```

(This is the assistant's preferences display)

TIP: Make an alias of the MSScanner software and place it in the Startup Items folder. When you boot up your Avid, MSScanner will automatically open and proceed to administrate write privileges for that particular Avid. Once this process is complete, hide MSScanner and boot up your Composer software.

WARNING! If you experience problems launching MSScanner, take the alias out of the Startup Items folder. Place an alias of the software on the desktop instead and initiate the program manually. Your system may have trouble expediting MSScanner as a startup item.

A Typical Scenario

You are a first assistant on a feature. The editor has an Avid in the adjacent room. In addition to your film equipment, you have your own Avid. Both systems are connected to the same media drives through the Media Share box. Many editing facilities are prepared for this event and should provide adjacent rooms with a 4-inch hole in the common wall to run SCSI cables through.

Now both you and the editor are connected to the same media drives. However, only one person can digitize at a time. My bet is that it's going to be you. The first thing you must do is limit the editor's access privileges to the drives by locking all but one of the drives on the editor's system. Allocate a partition with the name "FX" or "Editor" on the editor's system. This process is one of the few perks as an assistant editor. Now you have all the power.

MOVING MATERIAL FROM THE ASSISTANT EDITOR'S STATION TO THE EDITOR'S SYSTEM

The Media Share system was designed to allow multiple systems to read the same media from the same drives simultaneously without having to create duplicate media. However, the project, with all its bins and settings, is not shared. You will have to create two similar projects, one on the editor's system and one on the assistant's system. The main difference between the two projects is that the assistant's project will contain all the Dailies By Day bins that are unnecessary in the editor's project.

Once you have created two similar projects, new bins are made throughout the shoot. The dailies are distributed into scene bins and moved over to the editor's system for cutting.

Moving a Bin (With Editor's System Shut Down)

STEP BY STEP

1) Create a new bin.

2) Save your project.

3) Hide the Composer software.

4) On your desktop, open your project folder and copy the new bin over to the Media Share partition. You can use any partition that you have write access to as a temporary transport vehicle.

5) Start the editor's system. When an Avid first boots up, it looks at all the media drives attached and recognizes the presence of new media.

6) Open the Media Share partition from the editor's system and copy the bin over to the editor's project folder.

Moving a Bin (With Editor's System Running)

STEP BY STEP

1) Create a new bin with new media.

2) Make a note of which media drive contains the new media, e.g. Drive One.

3) Save your project.

4) Hide the Composer software.

5) On your desktop, open your project folder and copy the bin over to the Media Share partition.

6) Hide the Composer software on the editor's system.

7) Open the Media Share partition from the editor's system and copy the bin over to the editor's project folder.

8) Drag the partition Drive One into the editor's trash, removing it from the desktop.

9) Bring back the editor's Composer software from hiding.

10) Open the new bin.

11) Under the File menu, select Mount All. Drive One will remount onto the desktop. The Composer software will be forced to re-look at this partition, recognizing that there is new media on Drive One.

WARNING! There are problems with certain versions of the Composer software involving Media Share. You may experience problems such as partitions dropping off the desktop, frequent corruption on media drive directories, or crashing due to the current software bugs. The Mount All function has become inoperative in some 6.0 versions. Using this function has even led to severe corruption in media drive directories. The Mount All function on the File menu has been de-activated in 6.5.3. Avid's suggested work-around requires that you mount partitions using AVIDdrive Utility or by restarting the computer. Avid resolved this issue in later versions of the Composer software. In the interim, run Norton on all partitions overnight with the Auto Fix and Bad Blocks preferences activated (see Chapter 20, Preventive Maintenance).

Moving Scene Bins

The assistant editor creates the scene bins. Once the dailies have been distributed into the scene bins, you have to provide the editor with a copy of the new scene bin.

Use a different bin name every time you move material over to the editor's system. If you try to move Scene 015 bin over to a project in which this bin already exists, you may end up replacing the original bin. Any changes to the layout or contents of that particular bin will be lost. Therefore, the assistant editor must be very careful while making any additions or changes to the editor's project.

STEP BY STEP

1) Label the new bin as Scene 015 Uncut New. Use a symbol or word in a bin's name ("uncut" or "*") to delineate whether the scene has been cut.

2) Close the new bin and hide the Composer software.

3) Copy the Scene 015 Uncut New bin over to the editor's system. You can either copy the bin onto one of the unlocked media drives or use a floppy disk. I often use the Media Share partition as a transport device.

4) Change the bin name on both systems to Scene 015 Uncut to signify that the bin has been given to the editor.

TIP: If additional material from Scene 15 is digitized at a later date, create a new bin with a unique name, e.g., Scene 015 Uncut Add. 6/15 or Moving Bin 6/15. You may use moving bins as temporary vessels in which to transport material from one system to another. Once the moving bin has been opened in the editor's project, simply move the desired material from the temporary moving bin into the original scene bin. Make sure to indicate that a change has been made to the editor's Scene 015 bin.

WARNING! Never open a bin that exists on a locked drive. Always remember to move/copy any bin from a locked drive before opening it in Composer. If you attempt to open a bin that exists on a locked drive, touch up your résumé and beg for forgiveness. A bin can open from a locked drive, but as you have already noticed, the Avid automatically saves a bin when you close it. If the drive is locked, no changes to the bin can be made. STALEMATE!

TIP: Make sure that all computers attached to a Media Share system have internal clocks set to the same time and date. The Avid stamps all files and bins with the current time and date. You may experience problems moving a bin from a system that date stamps a bin with a time and date that has not yet occurred according to the destination system's internal clock. For example: If the assistant's system is set to 2:00 p.m. and the editor's system reads 1:00 p.m. and you move a bin from your Avid to the editor's Avid, the bin will actually exist in the future according to the editor's system.

CHAPTER 10
FIBRE CHANNEL

CHAPTER OUTLINE

SHARED STORAGE

Most computers operate alone. They are designed to read and write information to and from devices such as hard drives, floppy disks, and CD-ROMs. These local disks are usually connected to only one computer. A shared storage system is designed to allow multiple computers to simultaneously access the same data. The entire shared storage concept is simple and extremely easy to understand and operate.

When digital editing systems were first introduced, they were all independent workstations connected to dedicated storage devices. Almost immediately, the ability for more than one person to work on the same project not only became a request, it became a necessity. Avid answered this demand when they teamed up with Transoft to create SCSI MediaShare in 1994.

Avid's first shared storage solution allowed a few workstations to connect to the same media drives at the same time. This technology was embraced by the editing community and by other industries. Shared storage became a standard item in digital editing rooms. However, the system was not without flaws. Specific design limitations restricted the number of connectable workstations and the speed at which the data flowed from the drives to the workstations. Data bottlenecks were not uncommon while pushing this new technology to full capacity. Transoft later developed its own shared storage system, Fibre Channel, and stopped manufacturing Avid's SCSI Media Share in 1997.

SCSI VS. FIBRE

Computers connect to each other and to external devices such as drives via some type of cable connection. Small Computer System Interface (SCSI) is a type of computer connection format. A SCSI-compatible computer or drive will be equipped with a SCSI-compatible plug that can be connected to a SCSI cable. Any device that is connected to one of these SCSI cables must be SCSI compatible. The SCSI format has been a standard in computer technology for many years. However, as technology advances and changes, so does the computer connection format. The world of technology and computers has been moving toward an ever greater need for accessing large quantities of information at high speeds. Our thirst for more has exhausted the SCSI capacity. Therefore, it was inevitable that the SCSI format would one day become obsolete. That day came when Fibre Channel arrived.

The difference between SCSI and Fibre Channel technologies is similar to the difference between the new technologies for computer modems and the Internet. When modems were first introduced, they soon became a necessity on almost every personal and commercial computer throughout the world. Modem speeds were slow at first, which limited the amount of data and the rate at which data was delivered. As the demands on this new technology increased, modems became faster and faster until one day they hit a ceiling when the phone lines reached their capacity. Given the phone line's maximum throughput, it soon became irrelevant how fast the new modems were. However, the public's thirst for speed only increased.

Internet and modem technology will soon meet this demand when they adopt a brand-new phone-line and modem format. The introduction of the new Digital Subscription Line (DSL) phone line promises to be faster and better than current phone line technology and even ISDN lines. However, you will need to install a new DSL phone line (*cable*) and purchase a new DSL-compatible modem (*hardware*).

The same is true for computer connection formats. As the demands on this new technology grow, companies continue to develop new technological breakthroughs that take us to the next level. Fibre Channel is a faster computer-connection technology that requires Fibre-compatible cables (*cable*) and drives (*hardware*). Fibre is, theoretically, ten times faster than SCSI and has a larger capacity. In the digital editing world, this advancement translates to more shared workstations and larger quantities of accessible media delivered faster and at a higher resolution.

> **WARNING!** Composer 7.0 is not compatible with SCSI MediaShare. There are no plans to link 7.0 with SCSI MediaShare.

FIBRE CHANNEL SPECS

Fibre Channel supports both channel and network connections and does not become congested due to multiple workstations. Fibre Channel is capable of transferring 100 megabytes per second in both directions simultaneously, regardless of the number of workstations on the network. This is why it is often considered to have a 200 megabyte-per-second capability. Fibre Channel can deliver terabytes of information/media to hundreds of workstations on a network. It is not restricted by Composer versions and is fully compatible with most systems.

TRANSOFT

Transoft Networks, Inc. (formerly Transoft Technology Corporation), founded in 1992 by Michael Klein and James Wolff, is a leader in Fibre Channel Storage Area Network (SAN) technology and currently the only company offering a Fibre Channel cross-platform (XPL) shared storage solution. Transoft's Fibre Channel is like a universal connector that supports many protocols such as ATM, FDDI, Ethernet, HiPPI, IPI, and SCSI. The following section outlines Transoft's Fibre Channel hardware and explains how to operate the FibreNet software.

Hardware

ARBITRATED LOOP

Fibre Channel Arbitrated Loop (FCAL) is a topology, the physical arrangement of network nodes and media within a networking structure. In the case of a shared storage network, the network arrangement is a loop, all nodes connected via a hub.

HUB

Media drives have limited numbers of external connections, which determine the number of systems you can connect to the devices. Multiple shared-storage systems may need to use a *hub* to expand the drive connection capacity. A hub is a small device that connects in the fiber chain between the media drives and the Avid. The media drives are looped together in a chain that connects to the hub that each Avid is connected to. The hub acts like a traffic cop in a busy intersection, directing the flow of media to the Avids.

DRIVES

Transoft's ProTOWER is a 10-bay, 90-gig, JBOD (Just a Bunch of Disks) storage solution using Fibre Channel Arbitrated Loop (FC-AL) as its interconnect interface. As many as twelve towers can be interconnected to one or two Fibre Channel loops to form a large disk-storage system.

Transoft's ProRAID-FC is a 20-bay, 180-gig, storage solution. Terabytes of storage are available by combining multiple ProRAID-FC devices.

CABLES

Fibre Channel cabling can be either copper twin-ax (20 or 30 meters between nodes) or fibre-optic (up to 10 km between nodes). There is no difference in performance between the two cable types, but the fibre-optic cable usually comes with a considerably higher price tag. Transoft has recently lowered the price of optical seats to the copper price.

CARDS

In addition to the administrating software and the fibre drives, your Fibre Channel system is not complete without an internal fibre card in your CPU. Transoft's FibreNet uses a 2,128 megabit-per-second FC-PCI Host Bus Adapter card in each workstation. This additional internal card is connected to the storage device by a fibre cable.

TRANSOFT SHARED STORAGE PRODUCT LINE

Transoft currently offers three scalable shared storage solutions:

- FibreNet Lite supports up to four workstations with up to 124 storage devices (Mac platform only).
- FibreNet Standard supports up to 126 workstations and/or storage devices (NT, SGI, and Mac platforms).
- FibreNet Pro supports up to 200 workstations and/or storage devices (NT, SGI, and Mac platforms).

All three products feature administrate read/write privileges and messaging between workstations. Transoft is currently developing a shared system that allows multiple writers to share a single drive, but has file-level locking.

Software

FIBRENET

One of the integral parts of a shared storage solution is the administrative software. Shared-storage administrative software is designed to assign read and write access privileges to each workstation on the network.

Multiple workstations may read but should not write to the same drive at the same time. Any attempt to simultaneously write to a drive from multiple workstations will result in a crash, freeze, corruption, damage, or loss of data. In layman's terms, it's bad.

Transoft's administrative software, FibreNet (formerly StudioBoss), simultaneously delivers large quantities of data at high speeds to multiple workstations. FibreNet administrates read/write privileges, which prevent users from writing to the same volume at the same time. It also mounts and unmounts drives, communicates between workstations, and refreshes itself periodically to automatically recognize the presence of new media. The software runs in conjunction with the Composer software. Each Avid on a shared storage system should keep the FibreNet administrative software running in the background during operation. Any workstation on the Storage Area Network (SAN) can administer the FibreNet software.

MEDIA ENABLER

FibreNet systems come with only one other piece of software. Transoft's Media Enabler software allows Avids to recognize Fibre Channel drives. Using Media Enabler is as easy as placing an alias of the software in your Startup Items folder.

Setting Up Fibernet

Setting up FibreNet is a fairly simple process, although the program has to be customized to your particular systems. This entails assigning and restricting access privileges to your drives.

FIBRENET PARTITION

The FibreNet software preferences are saved as a FibreNet database file. The FN database file lives in its own tiny, hidden partition. One of the shared drives must have a partition with a minimum of 10 megabytes exclusively devoted to the database and should be labeled with the exact name "FN Database." All stations must have read access to this partition. To view the FN Database partition, uncheck Hide Database Volumes from the Administration menu in the FibreNet software. Transoft recommends keeping the FN Database partition hidden to prevent any information to be inadvertently written to it.

WARNING! Using the FibreNet Database partition for any other purpose may destroy the data. Do not use the FN Database partition to move bins.

STARTING FIBRENET

The FibreNet software should be installed on the hard drive of each computer on the network. Make an alias of the FibreNet software and place it in the Startup Items folder. When you boot up your Avid, FibreNet will automatically open and proceed to administrate read/write privileges for that particular Avid. Once this process is complete, hide the FibreNet application and launch your Composer software.

The Media Enabler software should be installed on the hard drive of each computer on the network. Make an alias of the Media Enabler software and place it in the Startup Items folder. Media Enabler allows each Avid to recognize Fibre Channel drives.

WARNING! If you experience problems launching the FiberNet software, take the alias out of the Startup Items folder and try launching the software manually once the Avid has already started up. You can bypass the FibreNet software alias in the Startup Items folder by holding down the F and C keys while you start up your computer.

Adding a Workstation

Each workstation on a shared-storage network must be logged in the administrative software.

STEP BY STEP

1) Open the FibreNet software.

2) Enter Administrative Mode from the Options menu. The password request box will appear. The default FibreNet password is 1111. The password can be changed from the Administration menu while in Administration Mode. Any workstation can be the administrator if you have the password.

3) Add or remove a workstation by selecting New or Remove from the Stations window. FibreNet gets the default workstation name from the Owner Name in the File Sharing control panel. The workstation's name can be changed, but must be unique to each computer.

STATIONS WINDOW

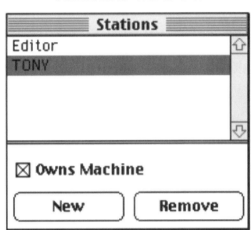

You can administrate access privileges for other workstations by highlighting their names in the Stations window.

The Owns Machine checkbox is automatically checked when the local station is selected. Since this is the workstation that I use, the box is selected. I can change the editor's access privileges by selecting Editor.

Drive Status

A drive's status is categorized as either locked, unlocked, or available. Unlocked drives are media drives that you have read and write access to. Locked drives have already been assigned to another workstation. Available drives are up for grabs.

• Unlocked
   The drives that have been assigned to your workstation are unlocked drives. You have read and write access to these drives. Your unlocked drives will appear locked from other workstations on the SAN. Other workstations may request access privileges to your drives (see Requesting Access Privileges below).

• Locked
   Drives that have been assigned to another workstation are locked drives. You only have read access to these drives. You may request access privileges to locked drives (see Requesting Access Privileges below).

• Available

   Available drives are unassigned unlocked drives or drives that are assigned to an in-active workstation. You can grab access privileges from an available drive at any time.

Assigning Access Privileges

The FibreNet software preferences are saved as a FibreNet database file. The FN Database file lives in its own tiny, hidden partition with the exact name FN Database. All stations must have read access to this partition. The FN Database contains the drive access privileges information.

STEP BY STEP

   1) Open the FibreNet software.

   2) Enter Administrative Mode from the Options menu. The Volumes window and the Volume Settings window will automatically open.

VOLUMES WINDOW

   3a) Assign access privileges by double-clicking on the drive icons in the Volumes window. The Volumes window displays all the active drives on the SAN. Each drive's icon box lists the name of the workstation that has write privileges, the name of the drive, and the available drive space. If you double-click on a drive that is locked, FibreNet will relinquish write-access privileges to you unless another workstation is active. If you double-click on a drive that you already have read/write access to, your name is replaced by "Available" until some other workstation grabs access to that drive. I have read/write access privileges to all but one of the drives. The editor only has write access to the Editors FX drive, which I am locked out of (signified by the little lock icon).

The only media created on the editor's system should come from creating dissolves and other effects. Therefore, the editor only needs access to one partition on which to render effects. The assistant's system should have access privileges to all the remaining drives.

3b) You can also assign access privileges in the Volume Settings window. This Volume Settings window displays the settings information for a particular drive. Highlight a drive in the Volumes window and check the Write box or the Mount (read) box to assign access privileges.

TIP: You may want to divide the editor's effects drive into a few partitions. After filling a drive with approximately 1,100 files, the Avid may have difficulty reading the Media Database file.

VOLUME SETTINGS WINDOW

Volume Settings	
DB Volume: FN Database	☒ **Write**
User Name:	☒ **Mount**
Volume Name: DRIVE A1	☐ **Auto-Update**
Volume Free MB: 1324	
Volume Modified: Sun, Aug 23, 1998 @ 11:09 AM	

WARNING! Mounting a drive using SCSI Probe or AVIDdrive Utility will bypass any previous read/write access privileges and may default a drive's status as unlocked to multiple workstations. Use the Mount Drive feature within the FibreNet software to mount a fibre drive.

REQUESTING ACCESS PRIVILEGES

Workstations on FibreNet's SAN can request access privileges to locked drives from other active workstations through the software's network messaging system. FibreNet's messaging system is completely internal and inherent in the fibre cable connections. It does not utilize Ethernet to communicate with workstations.

STEP BY STEP

1) Open the FibreNet software.

2) Double-click a locked drive in the Volumes window. If the workstation with

write access is inactive (shutdown), write access is granted. If the workstation with write access is logged into the FibreNet system, the access request box appears.

MESSAGING REQUEST BOX

3) Type a message, if desired, or just select Request.

4) The editor's workstation will soon receive this message and have the option to either grant or deny the request. A message will come back to you with their response. If the editor grants your request, the editor's workstation will relinquish write privileges to you.

WARNING! Only one workstation at a time should have write-access privileges to a drive.

Moving Material from the Assistant Editor's Station to the Editor's System

Shared storage systems were designed to allow multiple systems to read the same media from one drive simultaneously, without having to create duplicate media. However, the project, with all its bins and settings, is not shared. You will have to create two similar projects: one on the editor's system and one on the assistant's system. The main difference between the two projects is that the assistant's project will contain all the Dailies By Day bins that are unnecessary in the editor's project.

Once you have created two similar projects, new bins are made throughout the shoot. The dailies are distributed into scene bins and moved over to the editor's system for cutting.

WARNING! Do not use the FibreNet Database partition to move bins. Using the FN Database partition for any other purpose may destroy the data.

MOVING A BIN (With Editor's System Shutdown)
STEP BY STEP

1) Create a new bin with new media.

2) Save your project.

3) Hide the Composer software.

4) On your desktop, open your project folder and copy the bin over to any drive you can write to except the FN Database partition.

5) Start the editor's system. When an Avid first boots up, it looks at all the media drives attached and recognizes the presence of new media.

6) On the editor's system, open the drive containing the new bin and copy the bin over to the editor's project folder.

7) Launch the editor's Composer software.

MOVING A BIN (With Editor's System Running)
STEP BY STEP

1) Create a new bin with new media.

2) Save your project.

3) Hide the Composer software.

4) On your desktop, open your project folder and copy the bin over to any drive you can write to except the FN Database partition.

5) Go to the editor's system and save the project.

6) Hide the Composer software on the editor's system.

7) On the editor's system, open the drive containing the new bin and copy the bin over to the editor's project folder.

8) Highlight the FibreNet software and select the drive that contains the new media in the FibreNet Volumes display window.

9) Select Update Selected from the Options menu. This forces the Avid to re-look at the drive and recognize the presence of new media on that particular drive. Fibre Channel workstations periodically update themselves automatically by reading the Media Database files. You may not have to manually update your workstation in order to recognize new media. The media may already be recognized by the other workstation on the SAN.

10) Hide the FibreNet software.

11) Bring back the editor's Composer software from hiding.

WARNING! Do not use the FN Database partition for moving bins.

WARNING! Do not use SCSI Probe in conjunction with Transoft's Fibre Channel and 7.0. SCSI Probe is good for mounting SCSI devices. Use the FibreNet software to mount drives.

IMPORTANT! See MOBs, Chapter 20, **Preventive Maintenance**.

VOLUME MAINTENANCE MODE

FibreNet does not come with a built-in disk-repair program. However, the software understands that you may be utilizing a repair program such as Norton or Disk First Aid. FibreNet may prevent you from performing repairs while FibreNet is running since some drives may be locked or hidden. It is necessary to place the FibreNet in Volume Maintenance Mode while using any disk-repair utility program. Volume Maintenance Mode deactivates FibreNet and allows access to all the drives on the desktop, including the hidden FN Database partition.

STEP BY STEP

1) Highlight the FibreNet application.

2) Select Administration from the Options menu to enter Administration Mode.

3) Enter the password. The default FibreNet password is 1111. The password can be changed from the Administration menu while in Administration Mode.

4) Select Volume Maintenance Mode from the Administration menu. The software will proceed to ask you a few questions to make sure you want to continue.

5) Perform maintenance on the system.

6) Return the FibreNet software to User Mode. You can restart the entire computer or manually re-launch the FibreNet software.

TIP: Keep an alias of FibreNet in the Apple Menu in addition to the Startup Items folder for easy access.

AVID MEDIASHARE

Avid's launch of its much-anticipated MediaShare Fibre Channel (MS F/C) had a very shaky start. When Avid launched its first MS F/C product early in 1998, significant limitations caused problems connecting multiple workstations to large quantities of storage. Avid has been struggling to compete with Transoft's Fibre Channel, which has been on the market since 1997. On July 10, 1998, Avid recognized the need for further testing when they stopped shipping their fibre shared-storage solution. Avid immediately instituted a rigorous product revamping and quickly resumed shipping their improved MS F/C on July 29, 1998. Avid is now confident in its product and hopes many productions will choose its shared-storage solution. Avid's MS F/C is capable of connecting nine workstations to 540 gigabytes of storage or three workstations with the same amount of storage at AVR 77. Avid continues working to improve this new product with plans to expand its capacity and make the administrating software easier to use.

WARNING! Composer 7.0 is not compatible with SCSI MediaShare. There are no plans to link 7.0 with SCSI MediaShare.

Software

One of the integral parts of a shared storage solution is the administrative software. Shared-storage administrative software is designed to assign read and write access privileges to each workstation on the network. Multiple workstations may read but should not write to the same drive at the same time. Any attempt to simultaneously write to a drive from multiple workstations will result in a crash, freeze, corruption, damage, or loss of data. In layman's terms, it's bad.

Avid's Fibre Channel software, Avid MediaShare, administrates read/write privileges that prevent users from writing to the same volume at the same time. It communicates between workstations and refreshes itself periodically to automatically recognize the presence of new media. The software runs in conjunction with the Composer software. Each Avid on an Avid MediaShare system should keep the administrative software running during operation. Each workstation on the network administers its own access privileges through the Avid MediaShare software.

TIP: Avid MediaShare 2.44.2 can*not* mount or unmount drives. Avid recommends using AVIDdrive Utility 2.0 to mount and unmount fibre drives.

TIP: Avid MediaShare software has the option to automatically refresh itself periodically. However, Dale Jones of Sony Digital Picture Editorial does not recommend activating this option.

Setting Up a Profile

Avid MediaShare saves read/write access privileges in a Profile. A Profile assigns access privileges to a specific group of media drives. Media drives have to be added or removed from a Profile before access privileges can be assigned. Each workstation on the network creates its own Profile, which administers access privileges for that particular workstation. Profiles on different workstations will not conflict with each other. If you create a Profile that requests write access to a media drive that is already assigned to another workstation, your workstation will request write-access privileges. If the request is denied, you will be granted read access. If the other workstation is shutdown, you will be allowed to steal access privileges. A workstation can have several Profiles (see System Maintenance later in this chapter).

Adding Drives

A Profile contains your drive-assignment settings for a set of managed drives. You must assign your shared-storage drives to a Profile and designate them with read or write access privileges. You can create many different Profiles for assistants, editors, or any other user. A drive can be added to a Profile by clicking on the arrow pointing to the Managed Volumes side. A Profile will not administer access privileges to unmanaged drives.

STEP BY STEP

1) Open the Avid MediaShare software.

2a) If you are creating a new Profile, select Create from the Profile menu.

2b) If you are adding a drive to an existing Profile, select Configure from the Profile menu.

PROFILE SETUP

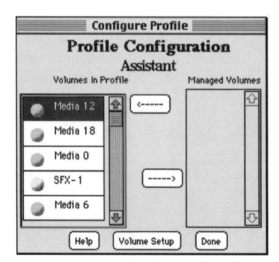

3) Add or remove volumes (drives) by clicking on the arrows.

WARNING! Eric Rigney at Sony recommends that you do not change drive or profile names. He also reminds you to label each drive with its own unique name.

Drive Preferences Display

Once a Profile has been created, you may assign access privileges to the drives that are managed by the Profile. The following is a volume status window that displays the Assistant Profile and the status of each of the drives that are managed by this particular Profile. The Assistant Profile has access to all of the drives that are displayed below. The colored ball next to the drive's name indicates the status of the drive.

Red ball   = Locked drive
Yellow ball = Read access only
Green ball   = Read/write access

MEDIA SHARE WINDOW

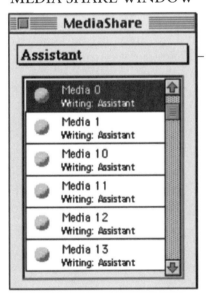

The current Profile is listed at the top of the MediaShare window. You can switch to a different Profile from the current Profile pop-up menu.

Assigning Access Privileges

Avid MediaShare software volume-access privileges are saved as a Profile. Each workstation on the network administers, saves, and stores its own Profile on its own hard drive. Workstations do not have read/write access to another workstation's Profile.

STEP BY STEP

1) Open the Avid MediaShare application. The Avid MediaShare window will open.

2) Double-click on each drive and define the Volume Setup.

MS VOLUME SETUP

You can also assign access privileges by selecting Create (for new Profiles) or Configure (for existing Profiles) under the Profile menu.

Requesting Access Privileges

Workstations on an Avid MediaShare network can request access privileges to locked drives from other active workstations. Avid MediaShare's messaging system works through an Ethernet connection, not through the fibre system. You can send a message to one workstation or to all workstations. You can use the Ping feature to check Ethernet connections between workstations.

STEP BY STEP

1) Open the Avid MediaShare software.

2) Select Users from the Workgroups menu to send a message.

3) Type a quick note to the editor's workstation and select Send.

MESSAGING REQUEST BOX

3) The editor's workstation will soon receive this message and have the option to either grant or deny the request. A message will come back to you with the editor's response. If the editor wishes to grant your request, he can accommodate you by relinquishing write access by altering his Profile.

If the workstation with write access to a drive is inactive (shutdown), you can gain access privileges to the drive by modifying your Profile.

> **WARNING!** Only one workstation at a time should have write-access privileges to a drive.

> **WARNING!** While using Avid MediaShare F/C, Apple Talk must be assigned to the Ethernet port instead of the printer port. No Ethernet connection = no MediaShare = no drives.

Changing a Profile

Profiles can be created, deleted, or modified. An existing Profile can be changed to reflect a different set of access privileges. New volumes can be added or removed from an existing Profile. You may want to completely delete a Profile and start from scratch by creating a brand-new Profile.

STEP BY STEP

1) Open the Avid MediaShare application.

2) Select one of the options under the Profile menu. You can create a new Profile, delete an existing Profile, rename a Profile, re-configure a Profile, or activate a Profile to administer access privileges.

PROFILE MENU

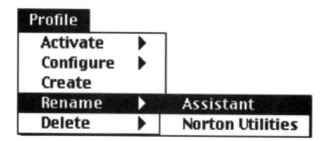

Moving Bins

Moving material from one workstation to another is similar to the procedure that is explained in the previous Transoft section. Please refer to the Step-By-Step directions in the previous section.

Avid MediaShare F/C workstations periodically refresh themselves automatically. You may not have to manually update your workstation in order to recognize new media. The media may already be recognized by the other workstation on the network. You can manually refresh a drive when you move media from one system to another by highlighting the drive and selecting Refresh from the Edit menu in the Avid MediaShare software.

EDIT MENU

Edit Profile	
Get Write Access	⌘W
Get Read Access	⌘R
Goto No Access	⌘N
Flush	⌘F
Refresh	⌘H
Refresh-Flush All	⌘A

System Maintenance

Avid MediaShare does not come with a built-in disk-repair program. However, the software understands that you may be utilizing a repair program such as Norton, StorEx, or Disk First Aid. FibreNet may prevent you from performing repairs while Avid MediaShare is running since some drives may be locked. It is necessary to have read/write access to all drives while performing maintenance.

You can create a specific maintenance Profile that unlocks all drives. This would be helpful while performing routine maintenance on your system. You can call the Profile "Norton" or "Maintenance". Avid recommends performing maintenance from one system while all other workstations on the network are shutdown.

TIP: Avid recommends using StorEx 1.2 (within AVIDdrive Utility 2.0) to test drives on the Avid MediaShare network.

TIP: Using the Clear Volume Management option in the software may eliminate certain Avid MediaShare malfunctions.

Shutting Down A Workstation

You have the option of maintaining the security of your Profile preferences even when your workstation is shutdown. The Exit Software screen appears whenever you quit the Avid MediaShare software. It provides you with three options, one of which retains the drive access privileges.

EXIT SCREEN

WARNING! There are drawbacks to using shared storage systems. You may experience problems such as frequent drive corruption, false media-offline messages, and occasional gray frames.

WARNING! Avid MediaShare requires that you stripe media drives on a network of two or more workstations.

CHAPTER 11
EDITING

CHAPTER OUTLINE

THE KEY TO EDITING

The most important step as you edit your project on the Avid is *think before you cut!*

THE AVID SYNDROME

New Avid enthusiasts suffer from a common syndrome. Editing on traditional film equipment provides you with the opportunity to think while you edit. The physical cutting and splicing of the film, threading the flatbed or upright, and rewinding a reel offers you the time to think about your next cut. Digital editing systems, because of their speed and efficiency, provide an instantaneous representation of an editor's every thought. This may cause an editor to try everything and ponder nothing. The speed and ease of digital editing systems *do* affect the way you work. I call this phenomenon the "Avid Syndrome."

HEALTHY, HAPPY EDITING

I once heard of an ancient medieval torture that forced a person to sit motionless on a one-legged stool while water dripped continuously upon their head. Sitting at an Avid for an uninterrupted, extended period may cause a similar strain to your body. If you find that working in front of a computer all day is taking its toll on your body, do not ignore it.

Take a break at least every hour. Stretch your hands and wrists. Stand up and walk around. Prolonged periods in front of a computer may cause pain, stiffness, and serious permanent conditions in some people.

HANDS/ARMS

A few years ago, I started experiencing a dull pain in my right hand and arm as a result of extensive use of the computer mouse. The repetitive clicking irritated the tendons in my hand, which led to pain and eventually numbness. I ignored the problem for lack of any reasonable solution. The mouse is an integral and necessary part of the Avid interface, and I was not willing to forego my career. As a result of the lack of attention I paid to my physical well-being, my hand and wrist worsened. Stiffness set in, followed by numbness that affected my hand and sent pain through the tendons in my arm. I literally thought I would not be able to continue using the Avid. Ironically, I had no discomfort while away from a computer. Nevertheless, the pain would immediately return upon briefly clicking a mouse button. Luckily, I found a solution in the Wacom artPad. This tablet takes the place of a mouse. The Wacom consists of a tablet and a wireless pen. The pad is sensitive to the pen's touch. The repetitive clicking motion is eliminated. So this story has a happy ending.

EYES

Rest your eyes as much as possible. Staring at a computer screen for prolonged periods causes eye strain. You may not realize that staring at monitors forces your eyes to focus at the same distance. In addition, the glare from the screen can cause dry eyes, fatigue, and headaches. Try not to zone out while staring at the screen. Close your eyes or go outside into the sunlight. I recommend placing an anti-glare screen on the fronts of your computer monitors.

BACK

Lower back pain is caused by many different ailments. Certainly, a healthy body will thwart most back-related symptoms. However, sitting on your ass all day at a computer ranks near the top of the worst ways to treat your body.

Make sure your chair has adequate support. Buy an adjustable lumbar support for your chair. You might find it easier to stand rather than sit at the computer all day. A standard film bench is the perfect table on which to set your Avid. Place your monitors behind the bench on coding tables. Get a comfortable high stool for times when you want to sit at your bench. This provides you with the flexibility to sit or stand as you please.

EDITING TIPS & TRICKS

TIP: If you want to make a few changes in an edited sequence, make a copy of the sequence! Alter the copy and not the original. You may want to go back to a previous version. Remember to name all cut sequences so you can find them later.

TIP: Audio Scrub allows you to listen to the track labeled with the hollow speaker icon. You can assign the hollow speaker icon to another track by holding the Option key while you point and click on any of the solid speaker icons.

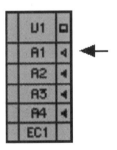

TIP: Audio Solo allows you to listen to only one audio track. You can assign the solo track by holding the ⌘ key while you point and click on any of the solid speaker icons. The speaker icon will turn green.

TIP: If the Avid says, "insufficient material to make this edit," the machine is telling you that you only need three marks to make an edit when you currently have four marks for this edit. The material in the source monitor is shorter than the distance between the in-mark and the out-mark in the record monitor. Get rid of one of your out-marks.

TIP: A perfectly good sequence may not play if there are too many unrendered effects. You may experience problems playing sequences with multiple video tracks that have unrendered titles or effects. The best way to resolve this is to render the effects.

TIP: The longer or more dense a sequence, the slower the Avid will perform. The system may appear sluggish while playing long sequences with many effects and titles. Try hiding the effect icons by deselecting them from the timeline hamburger menu. You may also type "playlength 1" in the console. This will allow you to play a one-minute section of a long sequence without experiencing any sluggishness. The playlength feature focuses all the Composer software's power on playing the segment immediately following the position bar. You can select different lengths, "playlength 2," for example.

TRICK: A bin window large enough to display all the items in the bin will automatically open by holding the Option key when you click on the bin zoom box (top right corner of bin).

TRICK: A bin window will automatically jump to the center of the bin monitor by holding the Option–⌘–" keys while the bin is highlighted.

TRICK: To open your project without any bins open, even if there were bins open the last time you shut down, hold the Option key while opening the project.

TRICK: You can determine if a portion of a source clip has been used in your sequence. Just load the clip into the source monitor and hold the Control key while you select the Match Frame button. The position bar will jump to where the clip is used in the sequence.

Measuring Clips

TRICK: You can measure the length of a clip or group of clips in a bin through the Console window.

STEP BY STEP

1) Open the Console window.

2) Highlight the clip(s) in the bin.

3) Select ⌘–I on the keyboard. The length of the clip(s) will be displayed in the console window.

REMEMBER! The Avid can*not* count footages above 9999+15 feet. The bin will display the number following 9999+15 as 00+00. Unfortunately, a 10005+00-foot reel will display as 5+00 in the bin.

TIMELINE

The Composer interface is made up of a dual-window display, button bars, and a Timeline. The dual window contains a Source material monitor and a Record monitor, which appear on your right edit monitor. The button bar, one row or two, is directly under both the Source and the Record monitors. The Timeline lives below the button bar(s) at the bottom of the edit monitor. The Timeline is a graphical representation of a sequence. It displays segments of audio and video as colored bars on separate video and audio tracks.

There are several useful Timeline options that you should be familiar with, such as Dupe Detection, Marked Waveforms, Scroll While Playing, and Auto Patching.

STEP BY STEP

1) Select the Settings button on the top of the project window.

2) Double-click on the Timeline settings.

3) Check the appropriate option box.

TIMELINE SETTINGS

Timeline Settings (Current)

Dupe Detection Handles   [1 Frame ▼]

☒ **Show Position Bar**
☒ **Show Effect Contents**
☒ **Show Marked Region**
☒ **Show Marked Waveforms**
☒ **Show Segment Drag Quads**
☒ **Scroll While Playing**
☒ **Double Click Shows Nesting**
☒ **Auto Patching**

[Cancel]

[OK]

Dupe Detection

The first option in the Timeline settings is not a check box, but a customizable pull-down menu for determining dupe handle lengths. Until 7.0, the Dupe Detection option was not customizable. It existed only in the Timeline hamburger menu as a function that either highlighted dupes in the Timeline or it didn't. The Dupe Detection Timeline setting offers you the option of determining dupe handle lengths.

A dupe is a frame or multiple frames of material that is used more than once in a sequence. Dupes are very important for film projects. On a film project, when the negative cutter cuts the negative, one frame at the head and tail of every piece of negative is, sort of, destroyed. When two pieces of negative are cut together, the negative cutter uses part of one frame immediately proceeding the shot to be able to attach another shot. Therefore, each shot in your sequence should have one-frame handles at the beginning and end for negative-cutting purposes. The Avid is aware of this requirement and will detect any dupe, or piece of material that is used more than once, including those handle frames. If you insert a new shot in the middle of an existing shot in your sequence, the dupe detection will highlight one frame at the head and one frame at the tail of the original shot where the splice was made.

Since the negative cutter destroys one frame at the head and tail of each shot, there is no other version of those frames in existence. The negative is the original, and once those frames are destroyed, they are gone forever. Therefore, the dupe detection is important because it notifies the editor when a dupe is required. If you have to include a dupe in your sequence, a duplicate negative is made at the lab prior to negative cutting so there is a copy of the original piece of negative.

Audio Waveform

The Audio Waveform options, Sample or Energy Plot, in the Timeline hamburger menu can be set to display only the designated portion between the in and out marks. You no longer need to wait while the Timeline re-draws the entire sequence.

MARKED AUDIO WAVEFORM

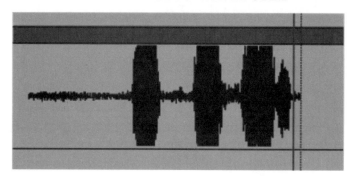

STEP BY STEP

1) Expand one or all of your audio tracks.

2) Activate either the Sample or Energy audio display from the Audio Data menu in the Timeline hamburger menu.

3) Change the project window to Settings.

4) Double-click on Timeline settings.

4) Check the Marked Waveforms box.

⊠ Show Marked Waveforms

Scrolling Timeline

The much-anticipated scrolling Timeline is now a reality. You have the option to have the position bar scroll through the Timeline as you play or output a sequence. The position bar will scroll through an entire sequence as long as the new Scroll While Playing option is enabled.

Auto Patching

Auto Patching automatically aligns audio tracks between source material and sequences. If you turn off the first track on a two-track sequence, a single-track source clip will automatically align itself adjacent to the available second track (the only active track) in the sequence.

Timeline Viewing

The Timeline zoom toggle has been redesigned with a slider (borrowed from the MCXpress) rather than the tradition obscure hash marks. Dragging the toggle increases and decreases the Timeline size like a zoom button.

ZOOM SCROLL BAR AFTER 7.0

TIP: Keystrokes ⌘–L and ⌘–K are used to enlarge or shrink the size of clips in a bin or tracks in the timeline. Since 7.0, these keys can also be used to zoom into an image in the source-side or record-side monitor. Just click somewhere on the image and use the keystrokes to zoom in or out.

AUDIO MIX TOOL

The Audio Mix tool has two main functions: It controls the audio levels for monitoring and outputting, and it controls the patching for monitoring and outputting audio. The Audio Mix sliders increase or decrease the volume for audio tracks on a clip or sequence. The Audio Mix patching controls designate mono, stereo, or direct-output configurations.

Composer can play up to eight tracks of audio, but it can output either four or eight discrete audio tracks, depending on the hardware limitations. Most systems are only equipped to output four discrete audio channels. Any assortment of eight audio tracks can be combined to output through the four output channels by utilizing the Audio Mix tool. Just because you can play eight tracks of audio in your sequence, does not mean that these tracks will flow directly and separately out of your system. The audio hardware determines the amount of discrete audio tracks. Outputting eight tracks from a four-channel Avid is like pouring water into a funnel. The tracks have to be directed through the available opening. This is very important when making outputs (see Chapter 16, **Outputs**).

AUDIO MIX WINDOW

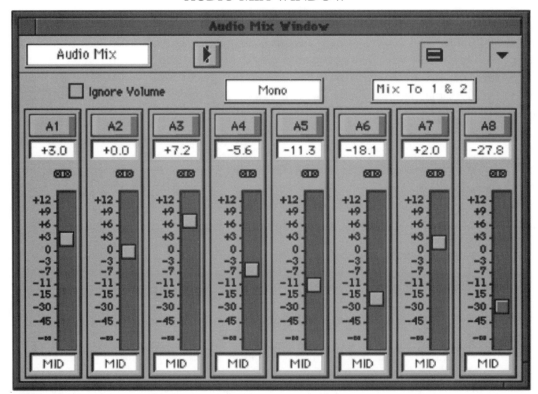

CHANGING AUDIO LEVELS (CLIPS)
STEP BY STEP

1) Select Audio Mix from the Tools menu.

2) Load a clip or subclip into the source monitor.

3) Click and hold on the corresponding audio-track slider and drag it up or down. The audio level change will affect the entire clip or subclip.

CHANGING AUDIO LEVELS (SEQUENCES)
STEP BY STEP

1) Select Audio Mix from the Tools menu.

2) Load a sequence into the record monitor.

3) Park the blue position bar on a segment of audio in the timeline.

4) Click and hold on the corresponding audio-track slider and drag it up or down. The audio level change will only affect the segment of audio that the position bar touches. If the position bar crosses over multiple audio tracks in the sequence, each segment that the position bar touches may be modified in the Audio Mix tool.

See the Automation Gain section later in this chapter for changing audio levels.

PATCHING AUDIO
The Audio Mix tool has three audio-patching options: mono, direct output, and stereo. Each setting directs the audio out of the Avid in a different way. Audio patching affects the direction of audio for normal monitoring while playing media *and* for outputs.

• Mono
  All audio tracks will be combined into two identical signals and come out of channel 1 and 2.

• Stereo Mix
  All odd-numbered audio tracks will come out of channel 1 and all even-numbered audio tracks will come out of channel 2. (Channel 3 and 4 can be substituted for 1 and 2 by changing the Mix To 1 & 2 setting to Mix 3 & 4.) Stereo mix only works properly if all tracks are panned left and right rather than all audio tracks centered. The center-pan audio settings can be found by changing the project window to Settings mode and double-clicking on Audio.

PROJECT AUDIO SETTINGS

- Direct Output

  All audio tracks can be directed to any combination of available channels. The channel selection box located below the slider can be set to Ch #1 - #4 (unless you have the 888 audio interface for outputting 8 tracks). If you have a 4-track sequence that contains production dialog on tracks 1, 2, and 3 with music on track 4, you can output to a videotape and still keep the music separate. The first three tracks can be directed to output through Ch #1 and the music track can be sent out through Ch #2.

DIRECT OUTPUT DESIGNATION

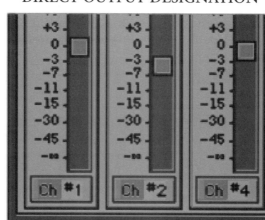

AUDIO GAIN RUBBER-BANDING

One of my favorite Avid features is audio rubber-banding. Audio rubber-banding has been a popular feature on many audio and video non-linear systems for years. Since composer 6.5, Avid has incorporated this very useful tool into the Composer Timeline.

The rubber-band feature provides a fast and easy way to modify audio tracks through gain-level control and ramping. It completely eliminates the need for adding edits on audio tacks.

The rubber-band feature can be activated by selecting Volume from the choices under Audio Data in the Timeline's hamburger menu. As you add audio key frames, instead of add-edits, you can map out a fade-in, fade-out, dip, peak, reduction, or raise in audio levels for a given audio segment.

Customize your Composer window or keyboard with the audio key frame button, which can be found in the command palate. Also, enlarge each audio track to see the dB levels more clearly. Remember to save this enlarged view.

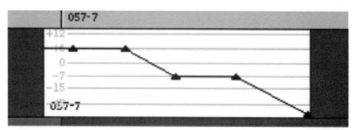

Audio can be raised or lowered by pointing and dragging key frames up or down. Holding the Command key while dragging an audio key frame will snap the volume bar to even dB increments. The audio key frames can be slid left or right by utilizing the Option key while dragging a key frame. This will allow you to modify a ramp angle.

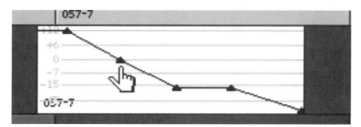

Multiple audio segments can be modified simultaneously by setting an in-mark and an out-mark around a group of clips. Any modifications to a key frame in the selected area will affect the entire group.

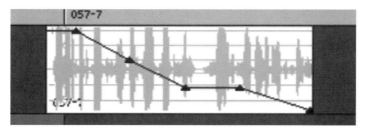

The energy or sample plot volume display can be used in conjunction with the audio volume display.

AUTOMATION GAIN

For the audio enthusiast, 7.0 offers real-time mixing on-the-fly. The Automation Gain window allows you to alter the volume levels of one or all of the clips in a sequence while it is playing. The adjustments made in this tool appear as mapped key frames when viewing the Timeline with the Volume option enabled. The audio can then be re-mixed manually by manipulating the key frames or automatically through the Automation Gain window again. For further flexibility, an external MIDI mixer, connected through the serial port, can work in conjunction with the Automation Gain window. MIDI mixer sliders provide a fully automated mouse-free mix. The HW (Hardware) button in the Automation Gain window activates external device connections.

MIXING ON-THE-FLY

STEP BY STEP

1) Load a sequence into the record monitor.

2) Select all, or a portion, of your sequence.

3) Activate the Volume display from Audio Data option in the Timeline hamburger menu.

4) Enlarge the audio tracks in the timeline.

5) Select Automation Gain from the Tools menu.

AUTOMATION GAIN WINDOW

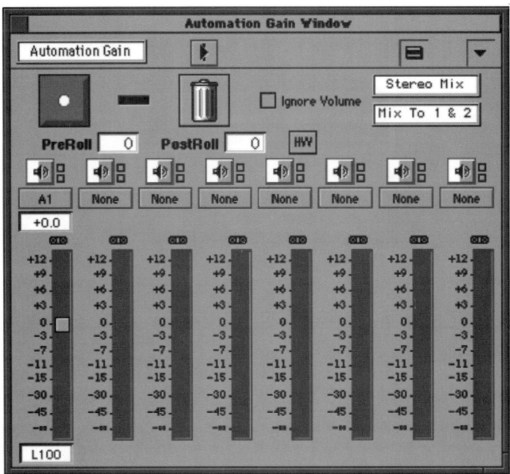

6) Set the preroll and postroll.

7) Set the speaker icons to monitor all or some of the audio tracks. The speaker icons allow you to monitor the audio tracks. A green speaker icon signifies a track that will be heard. You can isolate one or more audio tracks by turning the speaker icons yellow just by clicking on them.

8) Activate the audio tracks. Select the audio track that you want to alter from the box directly under the speaker icon.

9) Click once on the big red button. The sequence will begin to play and record the audio level changes made in the Automation Gain window. You can use the in and out marks to isolate a specific segment for mixing.

10) Drag the audio-level slider up and down as the sequence plays. The movements will be recorded as key frames in the Timeline. You can alter one or all of the audio tracks as the sequence plays.

11) Click once on the big red button to stop recording your mix. You can stop at any point in the sequence. Do not stop the Automation Gain tool by clicking the on the trashcan icon. The trashcan will delete the current record of moves.

12) Listen to the sequence.

13) Continue mixing the sequence. You can start and stop the Automation Gain tool at any point in the sequence. The audio levels are recorded as key frames in the timeline and can be re-mixed by re-recording over a section. The key frames can also be manually altered directly in the timeline (see Audio Gain Rubber-Banding above).

AUDIO KEY FRAMES

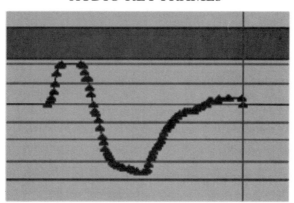

AUDIO EQ

The EQ Tool offers semi real-time previewing of effects, including an array of built-in audio filters. With a click of your mouse, you can instantly create the effect of someone talking on the phone. The EQ Tool works like any home stereo or car graphic equalizer. It is designed to limit and/or boost audio frequency bands in high, mid, and low ranges.

EQ WINDOW

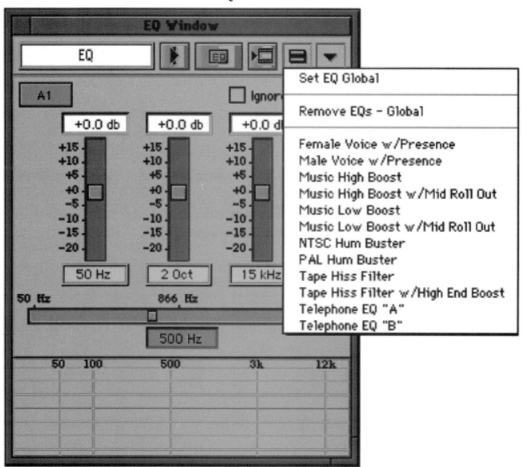

STEP BY STEP

1) Select Audio EQ from the Tools menu.

2) Load a sequence into the record monitor.

3) Park the blue position bar on a segment of audio in the Timeline.

4a) Slide the EQ frequency-band sliders up or down. The equalization change will only affect the segment that the position bar touches. An icon will automatically appear on the selected audio segment in the Timeline.

4b) Click on the EQ hamburger menu and select a filter from the list. An icon will automatically appear on the selected audio segment in the Timeline.

5) Preview the equalization change.

AUDIOSUITE

AudioSuite is an audio sweetening tool that applies filters to a sequence's audio. The AudioSuite tool allows you to access several built-in audio effects and unlimited third-party plug-in audio effects. The AudioSuite tool places the audio effect directly on the segment in the timeline and allows you to preview the native or third-party audio effect in real-time.

AudioSuite works in conjunction with the DAE (Digital Audio Engine). The DAE is a separate application that lives in the system folder on your hard drive. The DAE application, with plug-ins, comes standard with 7.0. Each time you open AudioSuite, the DAE application launches and connects to the AudioSuite Window.

Adding AudioSuite Filters

STEP BY STEP

1) Select AudioSuite from the Tools menu. Watch the status display as the DAE and built-in plug-ins launch and connect.

2) Park the position bar on an audio segment in your Timeline.

AUDIOSUITE WINDOW

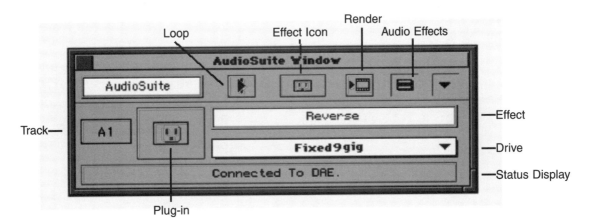

3) Select a track in the AudioSuite Window. The diagram above is set to track A1.

4) Choose an effect. The diagram above has selected the Reverse effect.

5) Click on the large Plug-in icon to enter preview/options mode. Depending on the type of plug-in, the preview mode may open an options window or a simple preview box (see example below). Some plug-ins such as Pitch Shift and Time Compression Expansion have more options for manipulating audio.

AUDIOSUITE PREVIEW BOX

6) Preview and render the effect.

WARNING! The DAE application requires a minimum of 12 Mb of RAM to launch and work properly. Make sure the system has enough available RAM for operating the Composer software in addition to the DAE application.

WARNING! Time compression or expansion audio plug-ins change the sample duration of the original clip. It may be necessary to create an audio mixdown for the audio portion prior to making an output.

WARNING! In all early versions of 7.0, the AudioSuite tool does not work with subclips. It only works with master clips.

AUDIO PUNCH-IN TOOL

Audio Punch-In is a digitizing tool that allows you to record ADR, or any audio, directly into a sequence. Audio Punch-In completely bypasses Capture Mode and places new audio clips directly in your sequence. The new audio clip appears instantaneously in your timeline on the tracks you select. A new master clip is also created and automatically appears in your bin.

AUDIO PUNCH-IN TOOL

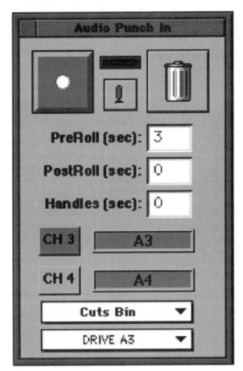

STEP BY STEP

1) Load a sequence into the record monitor.

2) Place an in-mark or set your position bar on your Timeline where you want the audio to start.

3) Select Audio Punch-In from the Tools menu.

4) Set the preroll, postroll, and handles.

5) Activate either one or two audio channels and specify on which track in your sequence you want the audio to be recorded.

6) Select the bin and drive from the pulldown menus.

7) Click on the microphone icon to open the Audio Tool to monitor the audio levels.

8) Click once on the big red button to start digitizing.

9) Click once on the trashcan to stop digitizing.

TIMECODE DISPLAY BOX

A floating timecode display box has been added with 7.0. This sizable window can display timecode, footage, or clip names on one or several lines of information. The box works with clip or sequence information.

JUMBO TIMECODE DISPLAY

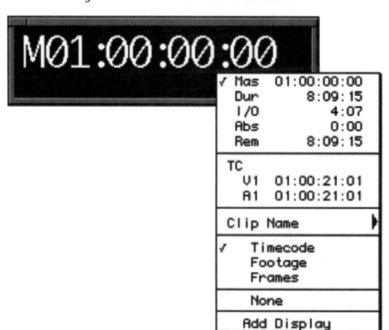

STEP BY STEP

1) Select Timecode from the Tools menu. The Timecode Box will appear.

2) Click anywhere in the box to reveal the options window.

3) Set the box to display the information. You can display information on several lines by using the Add Display option or remove lines of information by using the None option.

PROJECT TIMECLOCK

One of the most distressing new features in 7.0 is the "big brother" time-clock. This work-flow meter records each task by category. The time spent digitizing, editing, rendering, going to the bathroom, and talking on the phone are recorded in a hidden report card. Now, where is the trust?

STEP BY STEP

1) Select the Info button at the top of the project window to change the project window to display the project info.

2) Select Usage from the project window's hamburger menu. The project window will display the project statistics.

3) Do not show this information to anyone.

PROJECT WINDOW/INFO DISPLAY

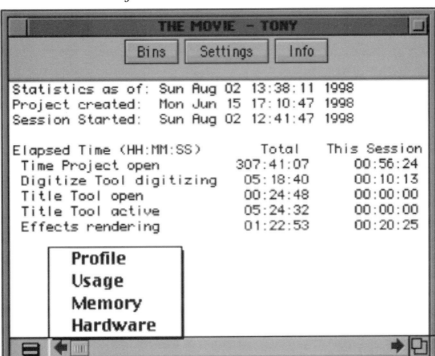

The information provided in the Usage display is stored in a Statistics folder within the project folder on the hard drive. This folder grows larger as the project progresses. If you are not using the project timeclock, you may choose to empty the Statistics folder completely. This will free some space on the hard drive and reduce the number of objects in your project.

TIP: Avid user Robert Brakey suggests creating a dummy file in Simple Text and naming it "Statistics" and placing it in the project folder on the hard drive. This will fool Composer into not making any more additional statistics settings files.

SCRIPT INTEGRATION

The Script Integration Tool allows you to integrate a script into your project for use while editing. The script, as it exists in Composer, can be used to link lines in the script with shots in your movie, delineate all the material shot for each scene, and edit. This feature has great potential, but given the complexity and time requirements for configuring an integrated script, the benefits may not be worth the investment.

The Script Integration Tool offers multiple-take previewing. You can grab multiple-lined script sections in the Script Tool for simultaneously playing the portions of all takes, one after another, that cover a particular portion of dialogue.

LOCATOR TOOL

The Locator Tool allows you to create different-color locators, add comments to the locator marks, and immediately access locators in a sequence from the Locator Tool. You can also display the frame in which the locator is sitting through the Locator Tool window. Locators can be sorted by column heading and deleted directly from the Locator Tool window.

LOCATOR TOOL

	Footage	Track	Comment
	12+03	V1	Good Reading
	13+09	V1	Good Reading
	15+13	V1	Alt. Reading
	19+00	V1	Alt. Reading
	20+06	V1	Take 1
	23+03	V1	Take 2
	23+11	V1	Take 3
	24+03	V1	NG
	25+11	V1	NG

Locators – THE MOVIE

INTRAFRAME™ EDITING

Intraframe™ editing, introduced with composer 7.0, allows you to edit within a frame. You can apply any of the numerous Composer effects to just a portion of a frame. Cloning, colorizing, custom masking, and animating portions within a frame is a mouse-click away. Wires can be erased, props can be moved, crowds can be expanded, and actors can be re-lit. Most of these effects do not translate into a cut list, but the new universal Grid Tool enables pinpoint accuracy with adjustable x/y axis locators and subfield positioning.

WARNING! The Intraframe functionality is not a standard item on all 7.0 systems. Intraframe editing is an additional feature.

MUSIC AND SOUND FX

It's a good idea for an editor to be familiar with different types of music. The director will greatly appreciate an editor who has the forethought to keep a small library of music and sound effects on hand.

MUSIC SELLS THE CUTS

Go to a record store and spend some time listening to CDs. Try to find a small selection of different music you might use for your project. Music without lyrics usually works best.

There comes a point in almost every project when the director is open to sampling different types of music for the movie. You may be asked to contribute by making suggestions and cutting in temp music. From your small library of CDs, try to find some temp music that best supports the mood of the scene. You may never use that particular piece of music in your final cut of the film, but your temp music track can substitute until the composer scores the movie. Music helps sell your rough cut to the director.

Many editors use other soundtracks as temp music. This is not only a good idea, but it really helps in screenings.

> **TIP:** Most of the temp music you will want to use in your project will be in stereo. However, it is not necessary to digitize music onto two tracks of audio. On your mixer, pan both channels of the music over to one audio-channel input on the Avid. Once you have digitized, center-pan the clip.

> **REMEMBER!** If you are digitizing directly from a CD, cassette, or DAT tape, set the pulldown switch to "x 1.00." Digitizing with the pulldown set at "x 0.99" speeds up the music or sound effect. Since your temp music may be used for the final mix, it is important not to alter the actual speed of the original recording. If you use altered music in the final mix, the sound department will not be able to sync up the original unaltered music to the same cut points used by the editor (see Chapter 8, **Digitizing**).

CANNED SOUND FX ARE NOT FRESH

Temp sound effects are tricky to use. Real sounds are usually much better than store-bought CD sound effects or "canned effects." There are many sound-effects libraries out there—some are good, and some are really bad. Most CD effects don't sound real. They tend to be cold, harsh, and much too clean. Layering effects in your sequence is one way to soften and legitimize canned sound effects. Filtering and equalization through the mixer also helps.

Some editors compile a collection of frequently used sound effects and music onto their own portable drives. You can transport your media from show to show and import audio directly into Composer from your portable drive.

TIP: Try to use the production sound as much as possible. You may want to periodically send the production sound mixer a wild-track wish list during production.

REMEMBER! If it went through telecine, pull it in at "x 0.99," sound effect or not. If it didn't, don't.

TIP: You can input music directly from an audio CD through a CD-ROM player for 44.1 kHz projects by using MoviePlayer to convert the tracks.

CHAPTER 12
TITLES

CHAPTER OUTLINE

Traditional film titles are still made by an optical house. This has not changed in Hollywood except for the fact that the optical houses now have much snazzier names containing either the word "digital" or the letters "fx." The type of computers used today to create and design titles and graphics can do just about anything. However, until recently, filmmakers did not have a fast and easy way to preview titles or graphics directly on the movie itself. Digital editing systems offer a valuable solution through their integrated title and graphics applications.

Traditional opticals are made through a photographic process of blocking and releasing controlled amounts of light through kodalith-type material. Traditionally, the filmmaker was unable to preview titles without this process. When the director was deciding whether the credits should run 6+00 feet or 7+00 feet, a photographic optical was made for his review. This costly and time-consuming process has been replaced by one of the best conveniences available in digital editing systems, the Title Tool.

Depending on your system model, most digital editing systems are equipped with at least a basic Title Tool. This tool allows you to preview your titles much the same way you create traditional opticals.

The Title Tool is a simple program that allows you to create graphics. This tool is great for building quick, temporary objects and titles. The Title Tool is a very handy addition to the Avid. However, it is not provided to create the same high-quality graphics that such programs as Photoshop, Illustrator, and After Effects are capable of.

The Title Tool creates simple graphics that can be cut into or laid over a sequence. This is a good way to determine the length and pacing of a title sequence. You can fade the titles in and out, add drop shadows, or animate titles. If you are lucky enough to have created a title sequence worthy of being close to what the director wants on film, save your title sequence, make an EDL and an optical list of your title track for placement, and output a tape for layout reference. Titles do not translate directly to a cut list. The size, font, and style of the titles you create will not be noted on any type of list. The position of the titles will be noted on the optical list. Assemble lists only indicate that an optical exists. The optical list will detail exactly where the title begins, fades, and ends by key numbers or ink numbers.

Graphics and titles are now truly uncompressed in real-time since 7.0. The Title Tool can now create PICT files rather than new media files. It is this PICT file that will be accessed (like a downstream key) each time you play the sequence. However, multiple or nested uncompressed title cards must be rendered before playing.

TITLE TOOL

The Title Tool is Avid's built-in titling and graphics feature in its Composer software. While Composer is launched, the Title Tool opens full-screen on either the bin or edit monitor. Many options and settings will appear at the bottom of the window. This elementary approach makes it easy to access the title options. The Title Tool allows you to save your settings by selecting Styles at the bottom of the screen.

TITLE TOOL SETTINGS

TIP: Before your project begins, create some stock title cards. I often find the need for a "Shot missing" card or a "Special-effect shot here" card. Maybe your film needs an "Eight months later" disclaimer to signify a time jump. Whatever the title, remember that it is temporary and will not magically appear on your negative.

Creating Titles

STEP BY STEP

1) Select New Title from the Clip menu to open the Title Tool. The Title Tool will open full-screen.

2) The Title Tool will automatically default to the previous type-style settings. Choose the font, size, style, and kerning you prefer.

3) Select a video or color background. If you intend the titles to lay over the picture, make sure you activate the video background option before saving your title. A green "V" signifies that the video background option is active. If you want a black or color background, deactivate the video background option and click on the background color box to select a background color.

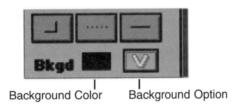

Background Color   Background Option

4) Make sure your titles do not extend off the screen. Check the Safe Title Area before saving your work. The Safe Title Area option is located under the Object menu.

5) The graphics you create in the Title Tool may appear jagged. To display the titles as they will appear once you close the Title Tool, select Preview from the Object menu. Preview mode will slow the operation of the Title Tool.

6) Select the font, style, size, and justification you prefer. Using the Typing Tool, type directly onto the screen. Use the arrow tool to move objects within the frame. Drag your cursor along the Title Tool menu bar to review the other available options.

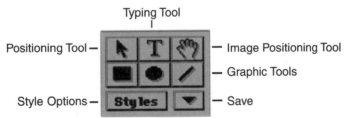

7) Save your new title in a bin designated for titles and graphics. When you close the Title Tool, the title will be saved into the open bin that you select. The title will appear as a two-minute precompute in the bin soon after the Title Tool has been closed.

The Avid considers titles as *precomputes* and will display them in your bin as such. A precompute is a media file directly associated with an effect. Although precomputes do not automatically load into your source monitor by double-clicking, they may be loaded by dragging them into the source monitor.

CREATING AN OPENING TITLE SEQUENCE

STEP BY STEP

1) Make a copy of your opening sequence.

Assuming that your titles lie at the beginning of your movie, subclip only the portion of Reel 1 that will contain titles. Adding titles to a sequence slows the Avid. In addition, the longer the sequence, the slower the computer performs. Try to work with short sequences rather than unnecessarily long sequences that slow down the system.

2) Label the opening sequence.

Save the title sequence in a separate bin. Make sure to differentiate the title sequence from the original reel. As the project progresses, you may permanently incorporate the title sequence into your cut reels.

3) Create the titles (see Creating Titles above).

4) Add a new picture track to your sequence. Titles should live in the second video track. The titles will not be visible unless the tiny monitor icon adjacent to the track indication box sits next to V2 rather than V1.

5) Drag the title into your source monitor. Align the source video track (V1) with the second video track (V2) on the sequence.

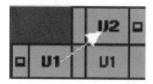

6) Cut approximately six feet per title into your sequence. This may become an extremely creative process depending on the complexity of your opening title sequence.

TITLE FADE-IN AND FADE-OUT

You may want to apply a fade-in and a fade-out for each title. The Avid makes this process easy for you. Just select the Fade Effect button while parked on a title. The dialog box will ask you for durations. Use this button instead of adding a dissolve.

FADE EFFECT BUTTON

ALTERING TITLES

Titles and graphics can be changed after they have been saved. As you cut titles or graphics into your sequence, you may alter them as many times as you like.

STEP BY STEP

1) Cut a title or graphic into a sequence.

2) Activate the track that contains the title or graphic.

3) Place the position bar on the title clip.

4) Enter Effect Mode.

EFFECT MODE

5) The Effect Editor window will open. Select the Title Tool icon opposite the T button.

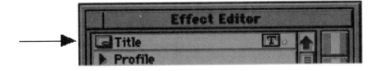

6) The Title Tool will open. Make changes to the title and close the Title Tool.

REMEMBER! Any changes to the title or graphic as it appears in the sequence will only affect the segment of the title or graphic in that particular sequence. The original two-minute clip will not be affected by this change. You can utilize this new title or graphic in your sequence as a source clip for later use.

WARNING! Unrendered effects may not appear on companion MediaShare systems. You may have to render title effects before transporting them to your companion system.

REMEMBER! Your titles will not translate completely onto an EDL. Some optical houses will require traditional film count sheets or Avid lists for counts. You should provide your title designer with a videotape output of your title sequence as a reference.

ROLLING AND CRAWLING TITLES

The Title Tool has the ability to create rolling and crawling titles. Rolling titles glide vertically across the screen. Crawling titles glide horizontally across the screen. The speed of the roll or crawl is controllable by the length of the clip.

Moving titles, as well as static titles, are created through the Title Tool. Titles that expand off a single screen can be accommodated by using the Roll or Crawl option in the Title Tool. Long lists of credits can be typed onto the screen, creating multiple pages of text, that will roll or crawl just by choosing either the Roll or Crawl option.

ROLLING/CRAWLING CREDITS

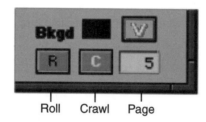

You can access a specific page in your rolling or crawling text by typing the page number in the Page box.

CHAPTER 13
SAVING YOUR WORK

CHAPTER OUTLINE

One of the most important procedures on a digital show is saving your work. Few things drive editors crazier than lost cuts. (Splices coming apart during a preview or directors snapping their fingers at cut points rank right up there.) However, losing work on a digital show is completely preventable. If you are careful and organized, you should never face the problem of losing your hard work on a digital show.

SAVE YOUR WORK

Continually save your work while you edit to prevent any loss of information. During the editing process, your work is *not* instantaneously saved in your project. The current edit decisions, or changes, are in limbo until a save is performed. If your system crashes, you will lose all your work since the last time the system performed a save.

You can manually save by selecting Save under the File menu (keystroke ⌘–S). The Avid does not allow you to perform any functions while the system is saving. The larger the bin, the longer the system will need to perform a save. You may manually save your work as often as you like, but saving every minute may signify a neurotic personality. The Avid also has an automatic saving feature called Auto-Save.

AUTO-SAVE

Auto-save is a feature of the Avid that automatically saves your work. To help ensure that your work will not be lost, the Avid is equipped with this helpful feature that periodically saves your work. You will notice when Auto-Save is active by a dialog box that periodically appears on your screen. The dialog box will identify the name of the open bin(s) with the prefix "Saving". The Avid does not allow you to perform any functions while the system is auto-saving.

You need to configure your bin settings to perform Auto-Save. The Auto-Save setting determines the duration of intervals between the automatic saves. The larger your project, the longer the Avid takes to save your project. When the auto-save begins, the Avid will prevent you from editing until it finishes saving. Any open, unsaved bins will automatically be saved in the attic (see Attic later in this chapter). Auto-Save will be your best friend and your worst enemy. It will be there for you by saving your hard work when the system crashes. It also activates at the most inopportune moments when the head of the studio wants to see a two-frame trim and up pops the friendly dialog box to say, "Hey, I'm saving here!"

Changing Auto-Save Settings

STEP BY STEP

1) Change your project window view to Settings. Click on the Settings box at the top of the project window.

2) Open the Bin settings.

3) Set the Auto-Save timer to your desired duration.

Remember that the Avid will not allow you to perform any functions during the saving process. Therefore, frequent Auto-Saves sound like a good idea, but they may impede your editing. I recommend setting the Auto-Save duration to 15 minutes. At most, you may lose fifteen minutes of work due to a crash. Use your own judgment and set the Avid to the most comfortable duration for your needs.

THE ATTIC

When the Avid performs an Auto-Save, the information is stored in the Attic folder. The Attic folder lives next to the Composer software on your hard drive (since Composer

7.0). It stores copies of the bins that were saved as a result of an Auto-Save. The Attic's capacity depends on the Auto-Save settings. When the Attic is full, the oldest bin backup is automatically eliminated, making room for the more recent backup.

Attic

A bin may not be opened from the Attic. If you need to retrieve a backup copy of a bin, you must first copy the bin from the Attic into your project folder on the Finder level.

PROJECT BACKUPS

Never rely on only one copy of your project. I can only compare this to leaving your entire family savings in a glass jar on the front porch. Digital editing systems by their design rely on computers. If you think computers are infallible, I have a Montage Editing System I could sell you. Computers crash, become corrupt, catch viruses, and malfunction, and when they do, you will be glad you kept a backup or duplicate of your project.

Your project folder contains the most important information for your show. All your edit decisions are saved in bins within your project. You can lose your media, but you can't lose your project. Media may be redigitized, but cuts cannot be automatically restored without a backup. Back up your project at least every work day before you go home. If you are worried about losing your work, and can't sleep, keep the backup disk in a safe-deposit box overnight.

My Floppy Ain't Big Enough!

You should always save your project on an external backup device. Storing your project backup on the same device as your original project defeats the purpose of securing the project backup. As your show progresses, the size of your project folder will increase significantly. Standard 3.5-inch floppy disks do not have the memory capacity to store feature-project folders. Before your film begins, make sure you have an adequate external storage device to store your project backups. There are several options: Zip drives, Jazz drives, magneto-optical, or SyQuest disks are all good solutions for your external backup device (see Chapter 2, **Avid Hardware**).

Backing Up Your Project

It is very important that you make a backup copy of your project each day. Label the backup with the project name and date.

STEP BY STEP

1) Make a project backup.

Your project lives on your internal hard drive in the Composer projects folder. Drag the entire project folder to your backup disk. The Mac will automatically copy the project folder to your disk.

2) Eject the disk!

Protect the backup device by disconnecting the disk from the host computer. Clearly label and store the backup disk in a safe place.

TIP: Save all previous copies of your project. Always keep a separate backup for each day. Do not replace previous project folders, cut bins, or reels with newer versions of your work. You may want to revert to a previous version.

If It Ain't Changed, Don't Save It

Compact Pro is a software program that compresses a file or files into a new, smaller, compacted file. The new compacted file contains fewer megabytes than the original files combined.

Compact Pro also has a valuable feature that recognizes the creation date of potential compacted files. This will allow you to only compact files that have been changed since the previous day. If today is Thursday, April 18, you can save all items that have been changed after Wednesday, April 17, or any other previous work day.

If your project has not changed substantially from one day to the next, you do not need to back up the entire project. If you have opened and altered every single bin throughout the entire movie, then you may want to back up the entire project. Otherwise, back up only the files within your project folder that have been changed since the previous backup. Since you already have a version of the project backed up, Compact Pro will locate only the files that have been changed since the most recent backup. This will significantly decrease the storage capacity required to back up your cumbersome project folder.

Backing Up with Compact Pro

You should back up your project each day before you go home.

STEP BY STEP

1) Close the Composer software.

The Avid will save your project automatically each time you leave the Composer software.

2) Open the Compact Pro application.

A lengthy dialog box will appear on the screen asking you if you would like to register your copy of Compact Pro. Ignore this instruction and select Not Yet in the lower right corner. An untitled Compact Pro file will automatically open.

3) Add the appropriate project files to the Compact Pro file.

a) Under the Compact Pro file menu, select Add.

b) Find the project folder located in the Composer projects folder within the internal hard drive.

c) Back up the new, or changed, files within your project folder. Highlight the check box that asks if you would like to save only those files created on or after the desired date. By selecting the current date, Compact Pro will only add files that have been created or changed today.

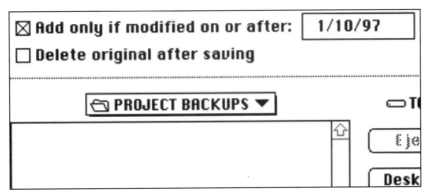

4) Save it!

Save the untitled Compact Pro file to your backup device. Clearly label the new compacted file with the show name and date.

TIP: When transporting compacted files to other computers that may not have Compact Pro, make sure you select Self Extracting before saving. Self-extracting files allow computers access to compacted documents regardless of whether they are equipped with Compact Pro.

BACKING UP MEDIA

The media on your show may or may not be backed up, depending on your budget. Hopefully, you will be lucky enough to have a producer who understands how efficient and cost-effective a media backup device may prove.

Media drives may become corrupt, burn out, or become damaged during your show. In this event, the lost media on the affected drive must be replaced. Redigitizing is a real-time endeavor. There is no faster way to do it other than doing it. Media backups are designed to decrease this lengthy procedure by storing the media on a device that can lay back media into your system faster than digitizing.

There are several ways to back up your media. A DLT tape backup is one common and reliable way to store a copy of your media. Sony Pictures Studios' Digital Picture Editorial in Culver City, CA, has an alternative tape backup system. The SDX-300 Advance Intelligent Tape System (AIT) uses Hi-8 tapes with a 25-gigabyte capacity. It boasts a transfer rate of 3 MB/sec. of uncompressed data.

Retrospect

Many types of media backup devices work in conjunction with Retrospect software, by Dantz. Retrospect is a program that organizes, categorizes, and systematizes the process of backing up media onto external devices. It coordinates the transferring of data from media drives onto your backup storage device and the restoration of information from the backup device back to its original location.

You can contact Dantz at www.dantz.com or via phone at (925) 253-3050.

CHAPTER OUTLINE

Conforming is the process of assembling a workprint to match a sequence in the digital editing system. When you reach the point when you want to screen the movie on film, the conforming stage begins.

CUT LISTS

Digital editing systems do not physically cut movies, people do. *Cut lists* are the maps that we use to link the digital world to the film world. Film cut lists are utilized for conforming the work picture, cutting the negative, and ordering the opticals. Generating cut lists is fairly simple and does not take much time. Learning how to make them properly does take time. The following section defines each type of cut list, explains how to make cut lists, and outlines the different list options and settings.

The following are all types of cut lists.

ASSEMBLE LIST - The assemble list provides a complete compilation of all the cuts in a sequence. It is used to conform your workprint or negative. The assemble list may contain footage, edge code numbers, key numbers, camera roll, scene, take, and length information for conforming.

PULL LIST - The pull list provides a sorted catalogue of all the material needed to conform a sequence. It displays all the material needed from each daily roll and collates the material into an easy-to-use, sorted list. The pull list eliminates the need to go back into a roll to lift a shot that is needed in the cut. The pull list is also used for re-conforming. It lists all additional material needed to add to the workprint. Since the pull list organizes material in the most efficient way for pulling shots, the list indicates the Assembly Number associated with each shot as it appears on the assemble and/or change list.

CHANGE LIST - The change list is used to re-conform a workprint. It describes the differences between sequences. The change list provides a complete compilation of all the material that must be added and/or subtracted to re-conform a workprint.

OPTICAL LIST - The optical list is used to delineate opticals counts. It may contain footage, key numbers, scene, take, and length information. Some optical houses are familiar with Avid optical count sheets. However, some optical houses still require traditional handwritten optical counts. Most of the effects in Composer do not translate to an optical list. The Avid is only capable of delineating simple effects, such as dissolves, on an optical cut list.

CONFORMING

I once assisted on a feature for which no workprint was printed until we reached the conforming stage. In that case, only the scenes that were included in the cut were printed. This was done in an effort to save money by not printing extraneous scenes that may never make it into the film. This alternative method did not prove monetarily beneficial. The detailed organization for printing only the shots in the film, edge-coding the picture at a late stage, and entering the ink numbers manually into the Avid delayed the conforming process. The producers were forced to hire additional assistants to accelerate the conforming. Once the studio got their hands on the film, there were more changes, which meant printing more scenes that were not in the previous cut.

Provided that you do not follow the previous example, conforming should proceed without a hitch. If this is the first time the workprint will be conformed, make an assemble list and a pull list. If this is not the first time the workprint has been conformed, make a change list and a pull list.

TIP: While conforming a workprint, activate the option Show Transition FX As Cuts. The assemble list will instruct you to butt-edit the transitions while still signifying the presence of an effect. (*This feature is broken in Composer version 6.12.*)

CHECKING YOUR WORK

When a project is ready to screen on film, the lists begin and accuracy is paramount! Cut lists are only as accurate as the information provided. All Avid cut lists are generated from the information in the bin, not from the burn-in information. The burn-in numbers are used to cross-reference the accuracy of the information in the bin. The Avid does not have the ability to notify you when burn-in numbers do not match the bin information. Therefore, it may prove helpful to spot check your burn-in numbers against the bin information and hard-copy reports, provided that you can rely on one of these sources to be utterly flawless (see Checking The Numbers, Chapter 8, **Digitizing**).

Check your burn-in numbers against your log files. If you have any doubt that the numbers are less than 100% accurate, check them against the print or negative or call the lab or negative cutter and ask them to read off the key numbers for a given punch frame. Punch frames make this process easy because there cannot be any disparity as to which frame everyone is looking at.

Checking the accuracy of the bin information in the Avid becomes especially critical for projects that never print film. Some low-budget features telecine directly from negative rather than from a workprint in order to save money. When it is time to cut the negative, a cut list is handed over to the negative cutter instead of a workprint. The negative cutter must then rely on the accuracy of the cut list as a guide while cutting the negative. Some negative cutters are now using a lock box for comparing the cut negative against an Avid outputted tape when no workprint is available.

Be very careful to avoid mis-cuts during the conforming stage. There are many little cuts and ample opportunity for something to be cut wrong. Try to correct any inaccurate numbers in the Avid before reconforming the picture to reduce the chance of mis-cuts.

Whether or not you are planning a temp dub for screening purposes, I recommend outputting the audio from the Avid to check the conformed workprint (see Chapter 16, **Outputs**). Do not wait until you get to a dub stage to find out that your workprint has been mis-cut. Make an audio output of the sequence and transfer the audio onto mag. Sync the mag with the conformed workprint to check the conform.

MAKING AN ASSEMBLE LIST

STEP BY STEP

1) Load the sequence into the record monitor.

2) Select Cut List from the Output menu.

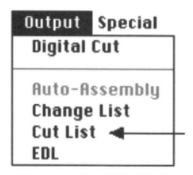

3) Select Get Sequence from the Cut List window. This will access the sequence in the record monitor.

4) Choose the options appropriate for your project (see Options later in this chapter).

5) Once the options are formatted, select View from the bottom of the Cut List Tool.

The Cut List Tool opens as it appears below. The options may be hidden until you activate the extended window view.

CUT LIST TOOL

The Cut List Menu allows you to activate the corresponding options window by highlighting the appropriate list. The adjacent activation button enables the list (see the Cut List Menu below). The Cut List Tool will not make any list unless at least one of these buttons has been selected.

CUT LIST MENU

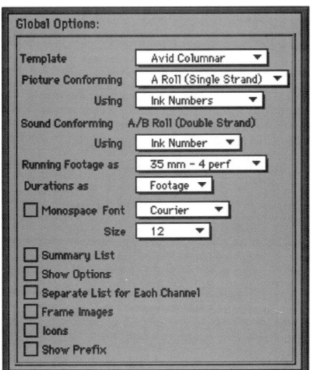

List Options

The Global function, the first item on the Cut List Menu, displays the options that affect all the lists.

GLOBAL OPTIONS

Either the Key Number or the Ink Number box should be activated for film cut lists.

Global Options

Template: This is a cut-list layout setting. Try Avid Columnar for making lists.

Picture Conforming: This refers to the way the negative is cut. Use A Roll (Single Strand) for 35mm projects. Use A/B Roll (Double Strand) for 16mm projects.

Using: Select either key numbers or ink numbers.

Sound Conforming: Select the appropriate setting for conforming your audio tracks.

Running Footage: Select the appropriate setting for your project. Most features use the 35mm - 4 perf setting.

Durations: The durations can be displayed by footage or frames.

Font: Try using Courier—it's easy to read!

Size: If your cut list does not fit on the page, try reducing the font size. I do not recommend going below font size 10.

ASSEMBLE LIST OPTIONS

WARNING! Show Trans. FX as Cuts is broken in Composer 6.12v10.

Assemble List Options

Key Numbers - For conforming a workprint using key numbers, or for any list provided to the negative cutter or optical house.

Ink Numbers - For conforming a workprint using ink numbers.

Lab Roll - Not necessary for most lists. Use only if you have lab-roll numbers included in your log files.

Camera Roll - Lists the camera-roll number in a column on the list. This information may be useful for the negative cutter.

Sound Roll - Use only when making lists for the sound department.

Scene & Take - May contain the same information as the Clip Name option.

Clip Name - Useful item on all lists. May contain the same information as the Scene & Take option.

Show Transitions FX as Cuts - This option will display the cut list with all the material needed to conform, instead of leaving a space for an optical. The list will still tell you where the optical goes so you can mark it up with Formaline tape.

The assemble list options can be carried through to the other lists' options. All subsequent list settings after the Assemble List settings contain the Same As Assemble List box. Once the assemble list options are set, you can save time by making all the other lists default to the assemble list settings.

PULL LIST OPTIONS

Defaults to Assemble List settings

<u>Pull List Options</u>

First Sort By - For setting the pull-list sorting preferences. You can sort by clip name, ink number, or key number.

Other Lists

Optical Scene Pull List - For making opticals. The negative cutter needs this so he can pull the appropriate material to be sent to the optical house. The optical house needs this to make the IPs.

Dupe List - Lists material that is used more than once in your sequence(s).

For an example of an assemble list, see the Change List section later in this chapter.

SAVING CUT-LIST SETTINGS

All cut list options can be saved via the Settings box at the bottom of the List Tool. You can save many variations of each type of cut list.

CUT-LIST SETTINGS LIST

| Assemble List |
| Change List |
| Dupe List |
| Optical List |
| Pull List |
| Tony's List |
| Untitled |

Settings: Tony's List | Save As...

CONFORMING OPTICALS

Digital editing systems allow you to preview an array of different temporary film opticals. Eventually, these film opticals have to be made on film by an optical house. Until then, opticals that are made on a digital editing system do not exist on film and therefore cannot be conformed into the movie for screening purposes.

The following are four ways in which to handle conforming opticals for preliminary screening purposes:

1) The optical house can make your opticals for you to cut into the workprint. This is the most expensive method and may prove wasteful if none of the temp opticals are used in the final cut.

2) You can slug the opticals with color leader or shot-missing leader. This is the simplest and least time-consuming method.

3) You can mark up the workprint to signify the location of opticals. You can use a grease pencil to mark the dissolves and fades, or you can use architect's tape, or $^1/_{16}$-inch Formaline tape, and neatly lay white strips of tape on the workprint. This common method does not accommodate complicated opticals such as blow-ups, repositions, or CGI shots.

4) The complexity and frequency of digital and/or optical shots in movies has increased dramatically during the past ten years. It is now common for movies to have in excess of 300 special-effect shots. Many filmmakers are now transferring temporary special-effect shots from videotape to film for screening purposes. Video-to-film transfers are costly and often don't look great.

I worked on a film once where the director demanded that the opticals be complete for the director's cut screening; however, the studio would not splurge for temporary film opticals. We found a more cost-effective solution by assembling the director's cut on tape. We onlined the movie and screened it on DigiBeta in a theater. It was quite a success. Not only were all opticals present, including repositioned and blow-up shots, there were no splices, dirt, or mismatched color problems.

CHANGE LISTS

The first time a workprint is assembled, it is executed according to an assemble list generated by the Avid. As the editor continues to edit, the workprint may be conformed to reflect the new changes. Each time the workprint is conformed after the initial assembly, it is done according to a change list generated by the Avid. (Also see Film Change Notes, Chapter 18, **Sound Mix.**)

The Change List Tool compares sequences and indicates whether to add, subtract, or move material from a sequence. The Change List Tool is similar to the Cut List Tool except for the addition of two sequence windows: one window for the old sequence(s) and one window for the new sequence(s).

The Change List Tool assumes that changes occur in order from the start of the reel. The sequence footage counter is cumulative. Therefore, if you delete 1+00 ft. from the picture, the next shot will fall one foot earlier. Any subsequent changes on the cut list account for the earlier one-foot change. The same is true for adding or moving material from the picture.

REMEMBER: Key numbers can be added or substituted wherever ink numbers appear in a cut list or change list.

Lists Are Inclusive

Avid's cut-list protocol is "inclusive." This means that the Avid includes all frames for footage calculations. The Avid considers that every frame has an address, and the address given for every frame includes the entire frame. For example, a one-foot shot that begins at 000+00 and ends at 000+15 consists of 16 frames or 1 ft. Additionally, if a change list indicates that a shot should be inserted at 365+05, the first frame of the new shot will start at 365+05, not 365+06. Avid's change lists all contain a reminder in the heading information that All Counts Are Inclusive (inside/inside).

> **TIP:** The Change List Tool can compare multiple sequences (see Rebalancing later in this chapter).

Naming Reels

The Change List Tool cannot recognize sequence names. It identifies reels by the number in the Reel # column in order to calculate sequence changes. The Change List Tool requires accurate information in the Reel # column in the bin info, especially when comparing multiple sequences. The Reel # column can be added to your bin display by modifying the bin headings.

The Change List Tool compares sequences as long as the Reel # column is filled in. Only enter numeric information for reel numbers. The change list must have this information while comparing sequences. The Avid is unable to interpret your alpha-numeric sequence name. It compares the corresponding Reel # from the old to the new sequence window.

REEL NUMBER COLUMN IN BIN HEADING

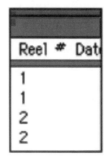

Making a Change List

STEP BY STEP

1) Select Change List from the Output menu.

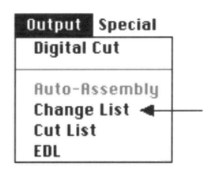

2) The Change List box will appear containing a space for Old Sequences and New Sequences.

3) Make sure the Reel # column in the bin contains the correct corresponding reel number (see Naming Reels above).

4) Load the old or previous version of the sequence by dragging the sequence from the bin into the Old Sequences window.

5) Load the new or most recently updated sequence by dragging the sequence from the bin into the New Sequences window.

6) Activate the Change List box.

7) Select View from the bottom of the Cut List Tool. The system will compare the edits from the old sequence to the new sequence and compile a list of all the changes between the two reels.

TIP: Multiple reels may be inserted into the Change List box. The system can compare more than one reel at a time (see Rebalancing below).

The following section illustrates exactly how change lists are created, read, and executed. I have created two dummy sequences with few differences between them.

OLD SEQUENCE

The following is an assemble list for Reel 1 (Sc. 25) 4/18 V3.

OLD SEQUENCE ASSEMBLE LIST

```
┌──────────────────────── Cut Lists ────────────────────────┐
│ Reel 1 (Sc.25) 4/18 V3   7 events      handles = -1        │
│ Picture 1                0 dupes       total footage: 38+08│
│ Assemble List            0 opticals    total time: 00:25:19│
│ -----------------------------------------------------------│
│         Footage  Duration      First/Last Ink   Clip Name  │
│                                                            │
│    1.      0+00   12+00   (NO EDGE NUMBERS)     Academy     │
│          11+15                                             │
│                                                            │
│    2.     12+00    6+03        025 -1041+09     25-3        │
│          18+02                     1047+11                 │
│                                                            │
│    3.     18+03    4+06        025 -1171+06     25A-5       │
│          22+08                     1175+11                 │
│                                                            │
│    4.     22+09    5+12        025 -1224+15     25B-2       │
│          28+04                     1230+10                 │
│                                                            │
│    5.     28+05    3+04        025 -1279+11     25B-3       │
│          31+08                     1282+14                 │
│                                                            │
│    6.     31+09    2+15        025 -1059+05     25-3        │
│          34+07                     1062+03                 │
│                                                            │
│    7.     34+08    4+00   (NO EDGE NUMBERS)     Academy     │
│          38+07                                             │
│ (end of Assemble List)                                    │
└────────────────────────────────────────────────────────────┘
```

The following is an assemble list for Reel 1 (Sc. 25) 4/19 V5. This is the same reel as the previous day except for a few minor changes. You can tell from the total footage that this new reel is shorter by four frames.

NEW SEQUENCE

NEW SEQUENCE ASSEMBLE LIST

```
┌─────────────────────────────── Cut Lists ──────────────────────────┐
│ Reel 1(Sc.25)4/19 V5    7 events      handles = -1                  │
│ Picture 1               0 dupes       total footage:38+04           │
│ Assemble List           0 opticals    total time:00:25:14           │
│ -------------------------------------------------------------------- │
│       Footage    Duration        First/Last Ink      Clip Name      │
│                                                                      │
│   1.    0+00     12+00     (NO EDGE NUMBERS)      Academy           │
│        11+15                                                         │
│                                                                      │
│   2.   12+00      5+13           025 -1042+01      25-3             │
│        17+12                          1047+13                        │
│                                                                      │
│   3.   17+13      1+14           025 -1294+09      25B-3            │
│        19+10                          1296+06                        │
│                                                                      │
│   4.   19+11      4+06           025 -1171+06      25A-5            │
│        24+00                          1175+11                        │
│                                                                      │
│   5.   24+01      5+12           025 -1224+15      25B-2            │
│        29+12                          1230+10                        │
│                                                                      │
│   6.   29+13      4+07           025 -1059+05      25-3             │
│        34+03                          1063+11                        │
│                                                                      │
│   7.   34+04      4+00     (NO EDGE NUMBERS)      Academy           │
│        38+03                                                         │
│ (end of Assemble List)                                              │
└─────────────────────────────────────────────────────────────────────┘
```

The following is a change list that compares:

Old Sequence   New Sequence

Reel 1 (Sc. 25) 4/18 V3   to   Reel 1 (Sc. 25) 4/19 V5

CHANGE LIST

```
┌─────────────────────────────────────────────────────────────────────────┐
│                            Change List                                    │
├─────────────────────────────────────────────────────────────────────────┤
│ Reel 1(Sc.25)4/19 V5      5 events         Old Duration    38+08          │
│ Picture 1                 3 insertions     New Duration    38+04          │
│ Change List - Reel 1      2 deletions      Total Change -   0+04          │
│                           0 moves                                         │
│ All Counts Are Inclusive (inside/inside)                                  │
│ ------------------------------------------------------------------------- │
│                                                                           │
│         At This                   For This                                │
│   ✓'    Footage    Do This        Length    First/Last Ink  Clip Name     │
│                                                                           │
│ _  1.   12+00   Trim Head     -   0+08     025 -1041+09     25-3          │
│         12+07                              025 -1042+00                   │
│                                                                           │
│ _  2.   17+11   Lengthen Tail +   0+02     025 -1047+12     25-3          │
│         17+12                              025 -1047+13                   │
│                                                                           │
│ _  3.   17+13   Insert Shot   +   1+14     025 -1294+09     25B-3         │
│         19+10                              025 -1296+06                   │
│                                                                           │
│ _  4.   29+13   Delete Shot   -   3+04     025 -1279+11     25B-3         │
│         33+00                              025 -1282+14                   │
│                                                                           │
│ _  5.   32+12   Lengthen Tail +   1+08     025 -1062+04     25-3          │
│         34+03                              025 -1063+11                   │
│ (end of Change List)                                                      │
└─────────────────────────────────────────────────────────────────────────┘
```

WARNING! The Change List Tool does not fully label reels in the change list header information. The example above is a change list that compares two different versions of Reel 1, however, the header only displays the new Reel 1 name.

The following section explains how to read this change list.

Reading the Change List

The Header

A Change List contains information in the header of the document, such as the sequence name, the track for which the list was made (in this case it is Picture 1), the type of list, and the reel number. The header also indicates the old duration and the new duration with a total change calculation. This Change List indicates that there is a four-frame difference between the old sequence and the new sequence. The Change List also indicates how many changes have been made. This Change List has a total of five changes with three pieces of new material and two deletions.

The header also indicates that All Counts Are Inclusive (inside/inside) (see Lists Are Inclusive above).

The Body
The body of a change list details the differences between the old sequence(s) and the new sequence(s).

The At This Footage column matches the footage counter on your synchronizer if the start mark is aligned with 000+00.

The Do This column instructs you what to do at this location.

The For This Length column describes the length of the piece of material which is being changed.

The First/Last Ink column provides the first and last ink number for the piece of material that is involved in the change.

The Clip Name column labels each shot.

The following are explanations for each of the five changes that appear on the Reel 1 (Sc.25) change list.

1) This first event tells you to remove 8 frames from the head of 25-3. I know 25-3 is the first shot in the reel because it starts at 12+00, directly after the academy leader. The next event does not occur until 17+11. This means that no changes occur from 12+07 to 17+11.

The Change List Tool can be set to display sections that do not have changes by deselecting the Show Only Changes box in the Change List options.

2) The second event tells you to add 2 frames to the tail of 25-3.

3) The third event is a new piece of material. The list instructs you to insert the new shot at 17+13. This new shot is 1+14 long. However, if you add 1+14 to 17+13, you get 19+11. But the list indicates that the new shot ends at 19+10. This is because the Avid includes the frame at 17+13 as the first frame where the new shot begins. The new shot is not added at the tail of the 17+13 frame, it is added at the head of the 17+13 frame. If the Avid instructs you to insert a new shot at 17+13, the first frame of the new shot will *include* the frame located at 17+13.

4) The fourth event instructs you to remove a shot from the sequence.

5) The fifth event instructs you to add 1+08 to the end of the last shot in the sequence.

Rebalancing

Motion pictures are edited in sections called reels. These 10-minute reels combined comprise the entire film. The longer the film, the more reels in a movie. The Change List Tool understands this concept and can accommodate changes between multiple reels.

The term "rebalance" in motion-picture film editing refers to the process of re-allocating material into 10-minute reels. If a scene is added or removed from a movie, the length of the 10-minute reel may be affected. Therefore, it may be necessary to move material from one reel to another in order to balance the reels back into equal lengths of 10 minutes.

Comparing Multiple Sequences

STEP BY STEP

1) Place all the old versions of your sequence(s) in one bin and place all the new versions of your sequence(s) in another bin. You can simultaneously compare all of the reels in a movie.

2) Make sure the Reel # column in the bin contains the correct corresponding reel number (see Naming Reels above).

3) Select all the appropriate old sequences from the first bin and simultaneously drag them as a group into the Old Sequences window.

4) Select all the corresponding new sequences from the second bin and simultaneously drag them as a group into the New Sequences window.

MULTIPLE SEQUENCES IN CHANGE LIST TOOL

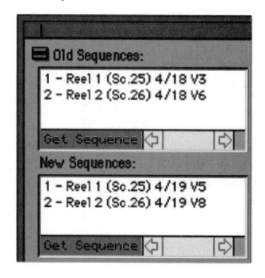

5) Activate the Change List button and select View to display the change lists.

The Change List Tool compares the reel(s) in the Old Sequence box with the reel(s) in the New Sequence box.

The following change list illustrates a rebalancing of material between Reel 1 and Reel 2. In this example, a piece of material has been removed from Reel 1 and added to the head of Reel 2. If you compare the old versions of Reels 1 and 2 to the new versions of Reels 1 and 2, the change list will tell you exactly where to place the shot in the subsequent reel. This same process applies for comparing all the reels in a movie.

The following is a change list that compares:

Old Sequence		New Sequence
Reel 1 (Sc. 25) 4/18 V3	to	Reel 1 (Sc. 25) 4/19 V5
Reel 2 (Sc. 26) 4/18 V6	to	Reel 2 (Sc. 26) 4/19 V8

REBALANCE CHANGE LIST FOR REELS 1-2

```
┌─────────────────────────── Change List ──────────────────────────┐
│ Reel 2 (Sc.26) 4/20 V5      1 event        Old Duration    38+04  │
│ Picture 1                   0 insertions   New Duration    33+13  │
│ Change List – Reel 1        0 deletions    Total Change –    4+07  │
│                             0 moves                               │
│ All Counts Are Inclusive (inside/inside)                          │
│ ----------------------------------------------------------------- │
│                                                                   │
│         At This               For This                            │
│  ✓      Footage  Do This       Length    First/Last Ink Clip Name │
│                                                                   │
│  _   1.  29+13   Move   Shot  –  4+07    025 –1059+05   25-3      │
│          34+03   to Reel 2 #1            025 –1063+11             │
│                                                                   │
│ (end of Change List)                                              │
│                                                                   │
│ Reel 2 (Sc.26) 4/20 V5      1 event        Old Duration    56+01  │
│ Picture 1                   0 insertions   New Duration    60+08  │
│ Change List – Reel 2        0 deletions    Total Change +    4+07  │
│                             0 moves                               │
│ All Counts Are Inclusive (inside/inside)                          │
│ ----------------------------------------------------------------- │
│                                                                   │
│         At This               For This                            │
│  ✓      Footage  Do This       Length    First/Last Ink Clip Name │
│                                                                   │
│  _   1.  12+00   Insert Shot  +  4+07    025 –1059+05   25-3      │
│          16+06   from Reel 1 #1          025 –1063+11             │
│                                                                   │
│ (end of Change List)                                              │
└───────────────────────────────────────────────────────────────────┘
```

Reading the Change List

The Do This column on the change list tells you that a shot has been moved from Reel 1 to Reel 2. It also indicates at which event it should be inserted. In this example, a shot has been moved from Reel 1 to event "#1" in Reel 2. The same applies if an entire scene is moved from Reel 1 to Reel 2. The list would then say "Move 5 Shots to Reel 2 #1."

If there are changes in a section that is being moved from one reel to another, the Change List will instruct you to perform the changes prior to moving the section.

Rebalancing the Wrong Way

If you only compare two different versions of the *same* reel in which material has been removed and added to another reel, the Change List will be unaware of the existence of any *other* reel in the movie. Therefore, the list will indicate that the material should be deleted instead of moved.

Using the same reels from the previous example, the following Change List was made by comparing the old version of Reel 1 to the new version of Reel 1 without including Reel 2. As you can see, the Change List thinks that the shot is no longer in the movie. It has no knowledge that the shot will eventually end up in Reel 2 unless Reel 2 is included in the Change List.

The following is a Change List that compares:

<table>
<tr><td><u>Old Sequence</u></td><td></td><td><u>New Sequence</u></td></tr>
<tr><td>Reel 1 (Sc. 25) 4/18 V3</td><td>to</td><td>Reel 1 (Sc. 25) 4/19 V5</td></tr>
</table>

CHANGE LIST WITH NO REBALANCE

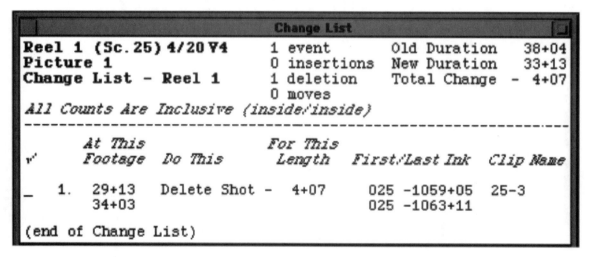

CHAPTER 15
EDLs

CHAPTER OUTLINE

WHO WANTS IT, WHO NEEDS IT, AND WHY?

An edit-decision list, EDL, is a compilation of timecode information generated by the Avid. It is used to conform video and audio for 30-frame projects and audio for 24-frame feature-film projects. It may contain source timecode, sound timecode, tape number, sound-roll number, scene and take, source table, and length information. On film projects, EDLs provide the sound department with the information they need to assemble the audio tracks.

EDLs are not used for cutting film. They are more common in the video world for 30-frame video projects. Video projects utilize EDLs to online picture and audio while film projects commonly use EDLs for conforming audio.

Turning Over To Sound

"Turning over to sound" is one of the most grueling challenges for a picture's editorial department. Before the digital revolution in Hollywood, this process was laborious; now it is almost unbearable. Postproduction sound has experienced its own digital revolution in the past few years. Unfortunately, the designers of digital sound-editing equipment and the designers of digital motion-picture-editing equipment have not always been in sync. We are now at a point where almost every post-sound department has a different way of doing things. Every sound editor has a different piece of digital equipment with different integration requirements, and each year the technology advances.

Regardless of what type of equipment your sound department decides to use, the following is a list of several elements you should be ready to provide. The sound-editing supervisor should provide you with a comprehensive list of detailed specifications.

The sound department may require from the picture department:

• The original sound rolls
• Timecoded videotape output for each reel with footage burn-in
• Timecoded audiotape output for each reel (DA-88 or DAT)
• EDL on a floppy disk for each reel, with a hard-copy printout
• Videotape copy of the entire show
• Reel continuity breakdown with exact footage and frame counts
• Wild-track log
• Color dupes of each reel

You should be prepared to provide the sound department with the above elements upon starting a dub or locking picture.

> **TIP:** Do not make outputs or EDLs before consulting your sound department. They may have detailed specifications for EDL options.

> **REMEMBER!** The Avid does not have the ability to generate EDL change lists.

Since you cannot generate EDL change lists from the Avid, you should provide the sound department with individual-reel videotapes that include visible burn-in footage numbers. The sound department can use these videotapes with film counts for conforming late picture changes. When late picture changes occur, and you know they will, you provide the sound editors with film change lists. The sound editors use the film change lists to conform the audio rather than re-assembling the audio from scratch by using a new EDL. Until someone invents a way to create EDL change lists, this procedure remains a fairly standard solution for digital shows.

> **TIP:** Most dub houses are not set up to print film footages on videotape formats. Therefore, the sound editor's dubs will probably have to be made in a telecine bay or with a Media Reader.

MAKING AN EDL

STEP BY STEP

1) Load a sequence into the record monitor.

2) Select EDL from the Output menu. If the EDL Manager does not open, manually launch the application from the desktop.

3) Select your EDL options. If you change any of the EDL settings after generating an EDL, the Update box will begin to flash. Clicking on the flashing Update box will remake the EDL according to the new settings (see Configuring EDL Settings below).

4) Activate the appropriate audio or video tracks.

5) Click the arrow button pointing from the Composer icon to the list icon. The EDL manager will generate an EDL for the sequence in the record monitor.

6) Save your EDL onto a double-sided disk and print your EDL.

EDL TOOL

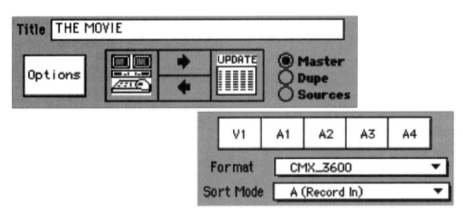

TIP: Most online editing systems can only read from a double-density disk rather than a high-density disk.

CONFIGURING EDL SETTINGS

The EDL settings are designed to provide flexibility in generating different types of lists. Many of the settings may not relate to your project.

Format

There are many different EDL formats; check with your online editor or sound editor before making the EDL. The following example displays a popular format, CMX 3600.

Sort Mode

There are several different sort options. Each determines the order in which the EDL is assembled. Check with your online editor or sound editor before making the EDL.

A-Mode sorts by record in-point.

C-Mode sorts by source reel number.

Master List

These settings affect the master list.

Master Start Event - This option starts numbering the EDL events at the designated number.

Reel ID Type - Set this to Tape for video track EDLs or Sound Roll for audio EDLs.

Timecode Type - Set this to Address LTC for video track EDLs or Sound TC for audio EDLs.

Convert To Numbers - Check this box if you want the source-tape name or sound-roll name to be displayed as a simple number.

Incl. Source Table w/Saved EDL - Check this box to display a legend at the bottom of the list that corresponds alpha/numeric tape and sound-roll names to the numbers that the EDL gave them.

Dupe List/Preread

These settings affect the dupe list.

Type - This gives you the option of generating a single dupe list or a new dupe list for each reel.

Dupe Reel Name - This option allows you to customize the B-Reel (dupe reel) name.

Starting Event - This option starts numbering the dupe events at the designated number.

Start Timecode - You can customize the starting timecode for the dupe reel.

Handle - This is used to set the dupe-reel handles.

Dupe All Transitions - Check this box if you want both sides of all transitions to be included in the dupe reel.

Comments

Check the appropriate boxes to include certain information in the EDL. I recommend including the clip names in the EDL.

Optimization

Check with your online editor or sound editor for specific EDL settings.

Standards

The default settings for the Standards options assume that this is a NTSC show in the USA using SMPTE timecode. If this is a European show, you can change the EDL to PAL.

Serial Transfer

These settings pertain to data transfers.

EDL SETTINGS

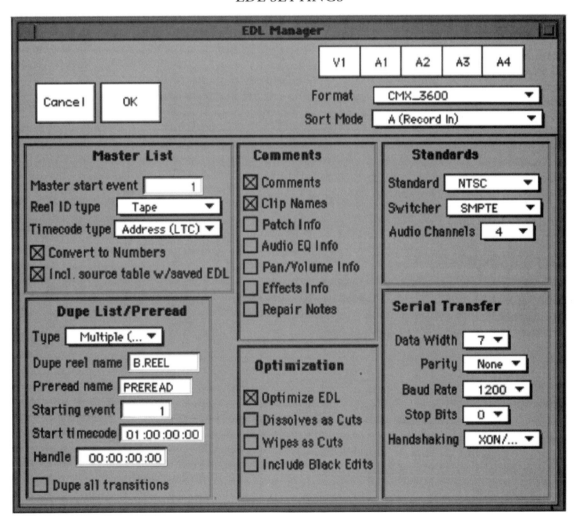

WARNING! Old Composer versions may crash while using the EDL tool. The old EDL tool was riddled with bugs and occasionally malfunctioned while trying to print or access the menu bar. The old EDL tool has been replaced with the EDL Manager in the newer software versions and promises to be more reliable. If you experience problems using your version of the EDL tool, it's probably not your fault. Use the separate application program EDL Manager as an alternative.

OMF INTERCHANGE

OMF Interchange is an independent file format that can store media and/or sequence ("composition" in the OMF world) information. An OMF (Open Media Framework) file can be read by any system that recognizes OMF files. More and more sound editors are requesting OMF audio files from digital editing rooms. Systems such as Audio Vision can readily access OMF audio files without the need to digitize anything. The compatibility and time advantage that OMF files present has spawned a revolution in delivering audio files from non-linear digital editing systems to post-sound departments.

NOTE: Composer 6.5 supports the importing and exporting of both OMF 1.0 and OMF 2.0 files. Composer 7.0 is compatible with OMF 2.0.

WARNING! Some systems will not be able to import dense or complex OMF files due to memory limitations.

CHAPTER 16
OUTPUTS

CHAPTER OUTLINE

FOR DIRECTORS, PRODUCERS, AND THEIR MOMS

The biggest mistake an editor can make is revealing the existence of a VCR attached to the Avid. Starting with the first day of dailies, the onslaught of constant requests for footage on tape begins.

My favorite request was from a production accountant who had a friend in another city who lived with a guy who designed the architecture for the building in which we filmed an eight-second shot. He asked if I would output the scene onto tape for his buddy.

More common are the actors or second-unit cinematographers who request material for their reels. Hopefully, the producers, the director, or the studio will set guidelines regarding the release of footage from the movie. It is always easier to refer someone to the studio or the director before they can get anything on tape.

Aside from the frivolous requests for tapes, there are many legitimate circumstances for which you may be making outputs during production. Directors may want to see rough cuts of scenes during principal photography. The set designers may need to view a scene to match backgrounds or check prop placement. Additionally, there will be many more occasions to output material in the later stages of postproduction.

When the editing process is almost complete, you will be making many outputs for the sound and music editors, music supervisor, composer, trailer house, publicity department, studio, optical house, mixers, and any festivals, competitions, or small towns on the southern coast of France. Unfortunately, each department will have its own particular format requirements. The vastly different output specifications can drive you insane. Everyone will have a certain preferred format with exact specs, some of which will have to be made at a dub house. This stage is very time-consuming and detailed.

SPECS

To illustrate the complexity and careful planning involved with providing each department the appropriate outputs they need to complete their job, the following are a few questions you might ask of the departments.

Possible Questions For The Music Editor
• Do you want one reel per tape or the entire movie on one tape? Due to the length restrictions for 3/4-inch and BetaSP formats, an entire movie may have to be outputted onto VHS or S-VHS tape.

• Do AB reels have to be connected?

• Do you need timecode burn-in or footage burn-in numbers?

• Do you need the timecode on the address track, VITC line 12 and 14, the Hi-Fi audio channels, and channel 2?

• Do you want the reels with or without temp music?

• Do you know we are using a 29.97 NDF video format?

   TIP: Ask each department to detail its exact output specifications in writing. Make sure *they* understand these specifications.

AUDIO

Far more choices have to be made while outputting audio than outputting video. Usually, a sequence will have one video track that is outputted onto a videotape. This same sequence may have up to eight tracks of audio containing different elements, such as dialogue, sound effects, and music. Whether you are outputting to a videotape or an audiotape, you should first decide your audio track assignment.

Composer can play up to eight tracks of audio, but it can output either four or eight discrete audio tracks, depending on the hardware limitations. Most systems are only equipped to output four discrete audio channels. Any assortment of eight audio tracks can be combined to output through the four output channels by utilizing the Audio Mix Tool. Just because you can play eight tracks of audio in your sequence does not mean that these tracks will flow directly and separately out of your system. The audio hardware determines the number of discrete audio tracks. Outputting eight tracks from a four-channel Avid is like pouring water into a funnel. The tracks have to be directed through the available opening.

Each department that requires a videotape or audiotape output from the Avid may have different audio-assignment requirements. The music editor may not want temp music. The composer may want to hear all or just part of the temp music. Depending on the various specifications, you may have to output a sequence several times to fulfill each department's requirements.

AUDIO MIX TOOL

The Audio Mix Tool has two main functions: it controls the audio levels for monitoring and outputting and it controls the patching for monitoring and outputting audio. The Audio Mix sliders increase or decrease the volume for audio tracks on a clip or sequence. The Audio Mix patching controls designate mono, stereo, or direct-output configurations.

AUDIO MIX WINDOW

(See Audio Mix Tool, Chapter 11, **Editing**, for changing clip and sequence audio levels.)

AUDIO PATCHING

The Audio Mix Tool has three audio patching options: mono, direct output, and stereo. Each setting directs the audio out of the Avid in a different way. Audio patching affects the direction of audio for normal monitoring while playing media *and* for outputs.

• Mono

All audio tracks will be combined into two identical signals and come out of channels 1 and 2.

• Stereo Mix

All odd-numbered audio tracks will come out of channel 1 and all even-numbered audio tracks will come out of channel 2. (Channels 3 and 4 can be substituted for 1 and 2 by changing the Mix To 1 & 2 setting to Mix 3 & 4.) Stereo mix only works properly if all tracks are panned left and right rather than all audio tracks centered. The center-pan audio settings can be found by changing the project window to Settings mode and double-clicking on Audio.

PROJECT AUDIO SETTINGS

• Direct Output

All audio tracks can be directed to any combination of available channels. The channel selection box located below the slider can be set to Ch #1 - #4 (unless you have the 888 audio interface for outputting 8 tracks). If you have a 4-track sequence that contains production dialog on tracks 1, 2, and 3 with music on track 4, you can output to a videotape and still keep the music separate. The first three tracks can be directed to output through Ch #1 and the music track can be sent out through Ch #2.

DIRECT OUTPUT DESIGNATION

Volume Control

Channel Selection

OUTPUTTING TO TAPE

The Digital Cut Tool outputs sequences from the Avid. Not all outputs have to be made with the Digital Cut Tool, but this handy function makes the process fairly easy.

Some of the more common formats used for outputting audio and video are VHS, S-VHS, BetaSP, and 3/4-inch tape. DA-88 and DAT are the most common formats for outputting audio. Your system does not have the ability to control a non-timecoded VHS deck. Therefore, it will be necessary to disable the Record to Tape option in the Digital Cut tool when outputting to any non-controllable, non-timecoded deck.

You cannot perform a digital cut onto an unformatted videotape unless you manually activate the record function on the destination deck. Without the presence of timecode, the Avid has no way of controlling *any* video or audio format during a digital cut. The Avid can only perform a fully automatic digital cut onto a controllable deck with a preformatted tape.

Black and Coded

"Black and coded" is the term used to describe the process of formatting a videotape. There are no frame lines, images, or timecode on a brand-new, unformatted videotape. A videotape needs an image, even if it is just black, for there to be any control track. Control track is the information on a videotape that defines where the frame lines exist. Any videotape, with or without timecode, will have control track as long as there is an image imprinted on the tape. Avid systems do not utilize control track information. "Blacking" a tape is the process of laying down control track onto a videotape. "Coding" is the process of numbering each frame with a number known as *timecode*.

Timecode information is different from control track in that it numbers each frame. Frame lines must be present before timecode can be laid onto any video format. However, there can be control track and frame lines without the presence of timecode.

Most video deck recorders have very similar features for formatting a tape. The Menu button on a deck will allow you to preset the starting timecode. The Set button will store this timecode number. As long as the black-burst generator is the only video signal fed into the deck, activating the Assemble Crash Record function will black your new tape. Remember to leave space at the head of a tape for bars and tone. Always place 30 seconds of bars and tone at the head of every tape. A one-hour tape should start with the timecode 00:59:00:00.

TIP: If your video deck has component connections, set the deck to composite while blacking tapes.

Digital Cuts

STEP BY STEP

1) Place your "black and coded" tape into the record deck. Make sure the deck is set to remote. The Avid works with many different types of controllable video decks and such audio decks as DA-88 and DAT machines.

2) Load and play your reference bars and tone clip and calibrate the record levels to "0" on your analog deck or -11 dB on a DA-88 or DAT. The Audio Tool has a Play Calibration Tone setting for generating a 1,000-cycle tone.

3) Load your sequence into your record monitor and select Digital Cut from the Output menu. For outputting to non-Avid-controlled decks, deselect Record To Tape in the Digital Cut options. You will have to manually engage the record function for non-Avid-controlled decks.

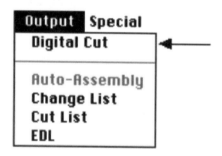

4) Select Entire Sequence and set the start time. Sequence Time will match the sequence's timecode with the corresponding timecode on the record deck. You can manually set the starting point on the deck by using Custom Time. You can start the output at the point at which the deck is paused by using Record Deck Time.

DIGITAL CUT TOOL

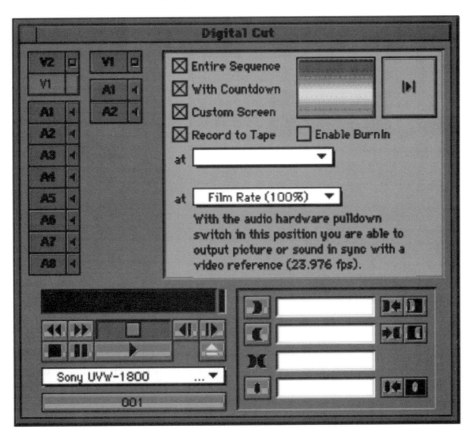

5) Activate the video and audio tracks you want to output. If there is a second video track, make sure the tiny monitor icon sits next to V2.

6) Set the rate to Film Rate (100%) for film projects.

7) Open the Audio Mix Tool and designate mono mix, direct output, or stereo output (see Audio Patching above).

8) Monitor the output through the mixer or, for a more accurate reading, plug your headphones directly into the record deck to check the levels.

You can manually push the Play and Record buttons on a deck while feeding it a video and/or audio signal. Manually recording onto an unformatted videotape is called a "crash" assemble edit.

Avid Countdown

The Digital Cut Tool allows you to add and customize an Avid countdown. If you select the With Countdown option, Avid's built-in eight-second countdown screen will appear prior to your sequence during a digital cut. You can also change the appearance of Avid's countdown screen or import your own countdown screen by selecting the Custom Screen option and clicking on the bluish square.

Modifying Sequence Start Time

The starting timecode for sequences defaults to 01:00:00:00. Each reel number should match the starting sequence timecode number. Set the starting timecode to the corresponding reel number: Reel 2 should start at 02:00:00:00, Reel 3 should start at 03:00:00:00, etc.

STEP BY STEP

1) Load the sequence into the record monitor.

2) Select ⌘–I on the keyboard.

3) Set the sequence start time.

Shift Big-Screen

This is a way to output sync video and audio without using the Digital Cut Tool. It is not *necessary* that you utilize the Digital Cut Tool for outputting audio and video. You can make an output by simply playing a sequence and activating the record function on the destination deck as long as all the connections have been made correctly. In software versions older than 6.0, the shift big-screen function has to be activated in order to send a NuVista signal out from the Avid. "Shift big-screen" is activated by holding the Shift key while entering Full Screen mode.

THE FULL SCREEN BUTTON

CHAPTER OUTLINE

OVERVIEW

Tascam's DA-88 has become a standard piece of audio equipment in editing rooms around the world. This digital multi-track player/recorder is versatile and fairly easy to use. As a source device, you can digitize audio dailies, wild tracks, music, sound stems, or any other audio cue into the Avid. As a digital recorder, the DA-88 is commonly used for outputting high-quality audio from the Avid.

One of the most common requests I received while writing the second edition of this book was to include a chapter on the DA-88. It is not necessarily a difficult machine to use, but the many little buttons and settings may initially be intimidating. It is not necessary to learn everything about the DA-88 since you will probably not be using the recorder to its full capability.

A few basic DA-88 functions that you should be familiar with are formatting a tape, playing a tape, and recording up to eight tracks. The following chapter outlines some of the functions you may be performing in your editing room.

DECK FEATURES

The DA-88 is a rack-mountable digital-audio recording device designed to record and play up to eight channels of audio. In digital editing rooms, the DA-88 is used for inputting and outputting high-quality audio to the Avid.

The DA-88 is fully compatible and controllable through the Avid. Just as your primary video deck works with the Avid, the DA-88 can be fully controlled through the internal deck controls in the Composer software. The DA-88 can be patched, using either an analog or a digital connection, directly to the Avid or with an analog connection through an external mixer, which gives you more flexibility and control of the audio levels. The DA-88 is fully SMPTE timecode compatible with an internal timecode generator and accurate external chase capability.

The DA-88 also features:

- A shuttle wheel that allows you to advance or rewind the tape at ¼ speed to eight times the normal playback rate
- A write-after-read four-head interleave system of data reading/writing
- CD-quality digital audio at either 44.1kHz or 48kHz
- Easy expansion of up to 16 DA-88s for a total of 128 synchronized tracks through a PW-88M cable (one cable required for each machine)
- SMPTE/MIDI/Chase-Lock Synchronization
- SMPTE timecode formats based on an internal or an external clock reference (video or word)
- Full implementation of the MIDI machine control (MMC) protocol and VTR (Sony 9 pin/RS-422) interface
- Audio pitch-control manipulation up to ±6%

Most commonly, the DA-88 is used to record the audio tracks from your Avid sequences. Without any loss of quality, you can output discrete audio tracks or combined audio tracks onto any combination of the eight DA-88 channels. Most four-channel Avid systems will be patched to channels 1-4 on the DA-88, but you can patch to any channels you choose.

The DA-88 does not have a remote/local switch. The deck will automatically respond to remote signals, although local manual-deck functions always take priority.

FRONT PANEL DA-88

TASCAM **DA-88**

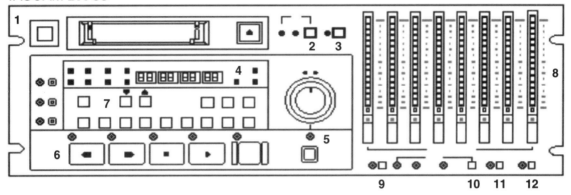

1. Power switch
2. Sampling frequency (rate) selection button
3. Format button
4. Alpha-numeric display
5. Shuttle
6. Deck controls
7. Display button and ▼▲ keys
8. Level meters
9. Chase button
10. Clock selection button
11. Timecode generate button
12. Timecode record button

REMEMBER! Make sure your DA-88 or PCM-800 (Sony's version of the DA-88) is equipped with an internal sync board. Both devices can be used in other environments without an internal sync card. Check with your rental or retail provider for deck specifications.

TAPES

The DA-88 utilizes the same Hi8 tapes used in portable camcorders for precise editing with seamless punching in/out accuracy. Many companies sell tapes specifically designed for the DA-88. These DA-88 tapes, or digital tapes, come with a higher price tag. The difference is negligible and either tape can be used.

There is a slight difference in play length between what is on a DA-88 tape box and the actual length. The following chart provides estimated DA-88 tape lengths.

Hi8	Actual record length in DA-88	
Tape lengths	NTSC	PAL/SECAM
20	18	25
30	27	37
45	40	56
60	54	75
90	81	113
120	108	—

WARNING! Do not use tapes longer than 120 minutes for NTSC or 90 minute for PAL/SECAM. Do not use Hi8 tapes that have been previously used for video recording.

PREROLL

Preroll is a deck's way of giving itself a head start. It is the amount of time a deck will retreat before a designated start mark. This buffer zone is designed to allow a deck to reach full speed before recording. The DA-88 default preroll time is five seconds. The postroll time is fixed at three seconds. The DA-88 needs slightly more preroll time than most video decks to get up to speed. I recommend using a long preroll time of seven to ten seconds. You may experience false starts while performing a digital cut with a short preroll time.

You can change the preroll in the Composer deck settings or directly on the DA-88. The following instruction applies to changing the preroll on a DA-88 with software version 4.01. You can view the DA-88 software version by turning on the DA-88 while simultaneously depressing the Fast Forward–Play–Record buttons.

Changing the Preroll

STEP BY STEP

1) Insert a tape.

2) Press the Display button to cycle the setting lights to *ABS*.

3) Push the RHSL (rehearsal) button.

4) Press both ▼▲ buttons at the same time to display the current preroll setting. The default preroll time is 5 seconds ("Pr. 00 05 00").

5) Use either of the ▼▲ keys to increase or decrease the preroll time.

You can change the preroll for any Avid-controllable deck directly in the Composer software under the deck settings.

FORMATTING TAPES

New audiotapes and videotape stock usually comes blank or unformatted from the store, although some places sell formatted videotape stock. It is not essential to format a DA-88 tape before recording audio. The process of recording onto a new, unformatted audiotape is commonly known as "crash" recording. Crash recording is as easy as loading a tape into the deck and pressing the Play and Record buttons; it is not a function that is controllable through the Avid. Crash recording is fine as long as timecode numbers are not important. Most of the time they are important.

It is necessary to format DA-88 tapes for making timecode-specific audio outputs from Avid. Purchase a supply of DA-88 tape stock before you start your project and preformat the tapes. Feature projects preformat DA-88 tapes to match the reel numbers. There is a separate tape, preformatted with the corresponding starting timecode hour, for each reel in the movie.

Formatting a Tape With a Preset Timecode

STEP BY STEP

1) Load a new Hi8 tape into the DA-88.

2) Rewind the tape to the beginning.

3) Set the Clock to INT. This will reference the deck to the internal timecode clock.

4) Press the Display button to cycle through alpha-numeric window options until you reach TC (Time Code). The small red lights above the Display button will alternate between options as you cycle.

5) Depress both ▼▲ keys simultaneously to display the current timecode format (30 DF, 30 NDF, 29 DF, 29 NDF). Cycle through the timecode format choices by using one of the ▼▲ keys. Select one timecode format for all your DA-88 recordings. Consult your sound department to determine the best timecode format for your project.

6) Press the Display button to change the display from TC to GEN (Generate). The GEN option is used to preset internal timecode.

7) Press either ▼▲ keys to set the timecode. Depressing the Display button in conjunction with either ▲▼ key accelerates the timecode advance. Allow space at the head of each tape for preroll and calibration tone. Preset Reel 1 for 00:59:00:00 and Reel 2 for 01:59:00:00.

8) Once a starting timecode has been selected, press the Display button to cycle back to the TC view. The preset timecode will temporarily disappear.

9) Press the Format button twice. Pressing the button once will cause the light to blink. Pressing the button twice will initiate the solid light, indicating that the deck is ready for formatting.

10) Select either the 44.1kHz or 48kHz sample rate (see Sample Rate, Chapter 8, **Digitizing**).

11) Press the TC REC button. The little red light will begin to flash. This button enables the DA-88 to record timecode onto the tape.

12) Press the deck's REC and Play buttons. The tape will begin to roll and the REC button light will begin to flash. Wait a few seconds as the deck gets up to speed and the REC button light stops flashing.

13) Press the TC Generate button. The alpha numeric display will begin counting, starting with the preset timecode number. The TC REC button light will stop flashing now. Allow the tape to format in real time. The deck will automatically stop recording at the end of the tape, then automatically rewind to the head.

DA-88 DIGITAL CUTS/AUDIO OUTPUTS

You can output the audio from your sequence to the DA-88 the same way you would perform a digital cut to a videotape. The only difference is that the DA-88 does not record video. It is not necessary to deactivate the video track in your sequence while outputting audio. In fact, I recommend that you perform a digital cut with the video track activated in order to see the output in progress. Not only will you be able to check sync, it's more entertaining.

If your sequence start time is 01:00:00:00, the DA-88 will search for the corresponding timecode on the DA-88 tape, just as a video deck would. However, the DA-88 requires slightly more preroll time in order to get up to speed. The light next to the record button will not stop strobing until the deck has reached full speed. If the deck does not reach full speed by the sequence start time, the record light will continue to flash and a warning message should begin to flash. If the output is not initiated properly, stop the output and begin again. Always verify that the deck has reached full speed at the beginning of an output.

Outputting to a Preformatted Tape

STEP BY STEP

1) Load the preformatted audiotape into the deck.

2) Rewind the tape to the beginning.

3) Set the Clock to Video. This will reference the DA-88 to the incoming stable video signal. The video signal originates from the black-burst generator on the editing system.

5) Press the Display button to cycle through the alpha-numeric window options until you reach TC. The small red lights above the Display button will alternate between options as you cycle.

6) Set the Avid interface switch to "x 0.99" for 24-frame projects and "x 1.00" for 30-frame projects.

7) Enable the appropriate DA-88 channels. The DA-88 will not record any information onto a channel that is not activated. You may record any combination of up to eight channels without affecting any information on a non-activated channel.

8) Calibrate the audio levels by playing the calibration tone from either the Audio Tool or from your own calibration Bars and Tone clip. Use the mixer to set the appropriate levels feeding to the DA-88. The DA-88 utilizes a digital (not an analog) VU meter. The calibration tone signal should fall at approximately -11dB on the green LED level meter.

9) Start the digital cut.

TIP: Place a pop at the head and tail of every sequence. You can always check where a pop occurs on the DA-88 tape in reference to where it occurs in your sequence to check for sync. If you are going to be make a mag transfer from the DA-88 tape, the pops will continue to be your best source of sync accuracy (see Academy Leader, Chapter 6, **Film Dailies**).

OUTPUTTING MORE THAN FOUR TRACKS

The DA-88 can record information to any one of its eight channels without disturbing the other seven channels. This becomes helpful while outputting five discrete audio channels from the Avid to the DA-88. Eight-track-playing Avids can only output four discrete channels due to hardware limitations. Therefore, only four discrete tracks can be output simultaneously. A fifth, or more track(s), has to be output during a second pass. You can only output eight tracks simultaneously from the Avid if you have the appropriate Digidesign 888 audio hardware.

STEP BY STEP

1) Open the Audio Mix Tool and select Direct Output. Individually patch the first four tracks in your sequence to the corresponding channels 1-4.

2) Calibrate the audio levels.

3) Turn off the fifth audio track in your sequence. Output the first four tracks from your sequence.

4) Rewind the tape.

5) Deactivate channels 1-4 on the DA-88. Activate only channel 5 on the DA-88.

6) Re-patch the Avid to the DA-88. Unplug the channel 1 cable leading to the input for channel 1 on the back of the DA-88 and plug it into the input for channel 5 on the DA-88.

7) Deactivate tracks 1-4 in your sequence and activate only track 5.

8) Open the Audio Mix window and patch the fifth track in the sequence to channel 1. Make sure none of the other tracks are assigned. The Avid will send the fifth track's signal out through the channel 1 cable, which is now patched into channel 5 on the DA-88.

9) Calibrate the audio for the fifth track onto channel 5 on the DA-88.

10) Re-output the sequence. The fifth audio track will be laid down in perfect sync with the other four tracks. You now have a DA-88 tape copy of your project's audio with five discrete audio tracks.

OUTPUTTING TO MAG

During the conforming stage on a film project, mag tracks have to be made from the Avid in order to screen the conformed workprint. The DA-88 is used to create audio master tapes that are transferred onto mag. One audio tape is usually made for each reel of the movie. These DA-88 audiotapes are sent to a sound-transfer facility to be dubbed onto mag. The mag tracks can be synced with the work picture for screening purposes (see Chapter 18, **Sound Mix**).

Each DA-88 tape must have 30 seconds of calibration tone at the head to allow the sound-transfer department to calibrate the audio levels. Just as a videotape has bars and tone at the head, before the program starts, your audio master tapes must have tone at the head. Always place a pop at the head and tail of each audio tape to guarantee perfect sync (see Academy Leader, Chapter 6, **Film Dailies**).

Once the sound-transfer department has made the mag, check it against the conformed work picture prior to any screening. Many things can go wrong in the process of getting the audio out of the Avid onto a DA-88 tape and through the sound-transfer department. The mag may come back out-of-sync, with audio drop-outs, or with unacceptable audio levels. If the mag is out-of-sync with the picture, check that you made the DA-88 tape properly. Check that the location of the pop at the end of the audiotape matches the Avid. Confirm that the tape was made at the correct rate. Make certain that the sound-transfer department is recording at the correct rate. If the mag has drop-out, ask the sound-transfer department to redo the transfer with fresh mag stock. If the mag has unusually high or low audio levels, check the calibration tone at the head of the DA-88 tape. Ask the sound-transfer department if they used the calibration tone in setting up for the transfer.

Some theaters are capable of locking a DA-88 deck to a projector. This can save time and money during dailies since mag tracks would not be necessary. However, most theaters do not have this technology.

For more information about TASCAM FAXBACK literature, call (800) 827-2268. ©1997 TEAC America, Inc. All rights reserved. 7733 Telegraph Road, Montebello, CA 90640, (323) 726-0303

PCM-800

Sony's answer to the DA-88 is the PCM-800. It is a much nicer-looking machine with white buttons on a black body. Other than the aesthetics, the major difference is that the PCM-800 comes standard with balanced audio in/out and a built-in digital interface rather than a separate digital interface. Most of the functions are the same, and you should have no trouble familiarizing yourself with Sony's device if you already have experience with the DA-88.

CHAPTER 18
SOUND MIX

CHAPTER OUTLINE

TEMP DUB

A sound mix ("dub") is the process of mixing all the audio elements onto a master copy on a mixing stage. A final mix is the last step in the postproduction process. A temp dub, or temporary dub, is the process of mixing the sound for an unfinished project. In the feature world, temp dubs are used to create a rough or scratch dub of the audio for screening purposes. Many motion pictures are tested before a recruited audience prior to the film's release. These screenings are useful for many reasons. They allow the filmmakers to witness an audience's reaction to the film. They also help the publicity department better determine how and to whom they should market the film. The preview screening can influence and decide the fate of a film; therefore, it is important that the screening goes well. Not only must the picture look good, it should also sound good.

The temp dub is like a miniature mix of the movie. The sound editors prepare rough or preliminary sound elements, such as background ambiance, foley effects, ADR, and sound effects. Sometimes temporary music is mixed into the film if the score is not ready. During a short temp dub, the sound mixers speed through each reel of the film. The entire process is quite similar to a final mix except for the amount of time spent on each reel and the complexity of the sound elements available. Once the temp dub master tracks are made, they can be used to screen the movie. Hopefully, the temp mix will provide you with a high-quality rough mix that does not detract from but adds to the overall film.

Full-length feature films are edited into approximately 10-minute sections called reels. The longer the film, the more reels you have. These reels are important when thinking about a mix. Sound mixers dub feature films in 20-minute sections called "AB Reels." An AB reel is comprised of two reels (see AB Reels, Chapter 19, **The Film World**).

Once a reel has been mixed, the mixing stage will provide a sound master copy of the reel to the picture department. There are several different mag formats that the stage can create. The capabilities of the preview or screening site usually determine the mag format.

TURNING OVER TO SOUND

The sound-editing department will require certain elements from the picture department prior to a temp dub. Depending on your sound-delivery protocol, you may be asked to supply the sound department with some or all of these elements: EDL, cut list, DA-88, videotape, OMF, Jazz, or DAT. It is extremely important, regardless of the format being delivered, that each item be clearly marked with *reel #, version #, date, TRT (total running time), LFOA (last frame of action), and name of project.*

(EXAMPLE)

"The Movie"
Reel 3 Version 4 Nov. 7
TRT: 00:10:02:13 LFOA: 903 +03

Any time picture changes are made after you have handed the sound elements over to the sound department, new elements have to be made. This process can become cumbersome depending on the amount of picture changes, the schedule, and the complexity of the sound-department delivery requirements.

Sound Specifications

The entire postproduction sound process consists of several departments, such as sound effects, foley, ADR or looping, sound editing, and music. Each department must receive specific material from the picture department before work commences. The process of delivering this information to these departments is known as "turning over to sound." Unfortunately, this process can be time-consuming and extremely detail-oriented. Each department may have its own specifications. The following is a list of possible items you may be asked to deliver to the individual departments while turning over to sound:

Video Output
Assemble List
Change List
Pull List
EDL
DA-88
DAT
LFOA List
Jazz Disc with Media
OMF Sequence

There is no uniformity in the type of videotape each department needs. Some departments use S-VHS while others only like 3/4-inch. In addition to the tape format, infinite other specifications need attention. A tiny missed detail can snowball into hours of down time and thousands of wasted dollars.

The following is an example of a videotape transfer request form.

VIDEO TAPE SPECIFICATION SHEET

TITLE: The Movie   REEL #: 3   VERSION: 4   DATE: Nov 7

S O U R C E   T A P E

QUANTITY   **FORMAT**

(1)   S-VHS
                 VHS
                 BETA SP
                 3/4"   NDF (√)   DF

TRT: 10:02   LFOA: 903+03

AUDIO

CHANNEL 1 Production Dialog
CHANNEL 2 Music and sound effects
CHANNEL 3 Comp of Ch 1 & 2
CHANNEL 4 Timecode

D U B   R E Q U E S T

QUANTITY   **FORMAT**

(1)   S-VHS
                 VHS
                 BETA SP
                 3/4"   NDF (√)   DF

AUDIO PATCHING   **TIMECODE**

CHANNEL 1 → Ch.1   ADDRESS TRACK (√)
CHANNEL 2 → Ch.2   LINE 12 & 14 (√)
CHANNEL 3 → Ch.3   CH. 2
CHANNEL 4 → Ch.3

BURNIN

UPPER LEFT   TOP CENTER   UPPER RIGHT
LOWER LEFT   BOTTOM CENTER (√)   LOWER RIGHT

Please place 30 seconds of bars & tone at the head of each tape.

Label each tape with title, reel #, version, date, and length.

DUPES

Most mixing stages dub films while watching a projected print of the movie. To keep the workprint in good condition and free from scratches and dirt, a duplicate of the workprint is made for mixing purposes. A duplicate, "dupe," is an exact copy of the workprint and is made by companies that specialize in film processing and duplication. Dupes are only as accurate as the workprint they are made from. Once a picture change is made to the workprint, the dupe has to be either conformed to reflect the change, or remade completely. The complexity of the picture changes will determine if it is cost-effective and time-efficient to conform the dupe rather than making a new dupe. Any material that is removed from the workprint has to be removed from the dupe. If new material is added to the workprint, these new sections have to be duped in order to add the material to the dupe. It is usually cheaper to conform a dupe while you conform the workprint rather than remake a new dupe. Sometimes time constraints may not permit you to conform the dupe regardless of the cost.

Some picture departments are responsible for conforming the dupes, and sometimes the sound editors are responsible for keeping the dupes up to date. Some mixing stages dub to a video projection instead of a film dupe. On these stages, a master videotape is used instead of a picture dupe. However, for feature film projects, it is preferable to mix to a dupe.

> **REMEMBER!** A film dupe should not be confused with dupe detection (see Dupe Detection, Chapter 11, **Editing**).

PICTURE CHANGES DURING A TEMP DUB

Sometimes picture changes are made during the mixing process. In the event that the movie has been changed, new sound elements have to be generated by the picture department. There are some exceptions. A minor film change can be manually made to the workprint or dupe at the stage. Many dub stages have film-change rooms located nearby for this event. If the change can be easily adjusted by the sound editors and mixers, no new sound elements need to be generated by the picture department. If a change was made on the mixing stage, the digital editing system in the cutting room will not reflect the change. The change has to be reported back to the cutting room and incorporated in the Avid in order to eliminate any further confusion.

FILM-CHANGE NOTES

Digital editing systems are capable of generating cut lists and change lists. Before the domination of digital editing systems, change notes were done by hand. "Film change notes" are handwritten detailed instructions for picture and track changes. They indicate whether material is added, moved, or removed from a reel. In some circumstances, it still may be necessary to generate film-change notes. Movies that are cut on film, sound editors that cut on mag, and some sound mixers may still utilize traditional film-change notes.

A film-change note is created when changes to the picture and track have been made. Actually, the change notes can be generated as you make the changes. The purpose of these notes is to make it perfectly clear what was changed. These notes should be accurate and legible. The change note itself is fairly simple and easy to understand.

Sometimes, even on a digital show, it may be necessary to create film-change notes. If minor picture changes are made during a dub or temp dub, it may be easier to create a simple handwritten film-change note rather than generate a change list from the digital editing system. The following is a example of what a basic film-change note may look like.

Reading Film-Change Notes

The Header
Each page of a film-change note should be clearly marked with the project title, reel #, version, and date.

The Body
This film-change note has three columns:

Column 1 - The reel's footage counter is listed in the Footage column. This footage matches your synchronizer.

Column 2 - Changes made to the reel are listed by footage in the Change column. The total length of each change is listed in the change column.

Column 3 - A brief description of the change is listed in the Description column. The description column helps you check that you are altering the correct shot. This also helps the sound department locate and decipher the notes more easily.

The following is an example of a film-change note with five events that affect one reel.

TRADITIONAL FILM-CHANGE NOTE

	Footage	Change + / -	Description
TITLE The Movie		**REEL#** 1 **VERSION** 3	**DATE** 4/18
1)	12+00		No Change
2)	567+09	-1+06	Trim Tail (Door Closing)
3)	789+01	+9+12	Add Shot (INSERT Dog's Foot on Crack)
4)	798+13	-0+05	Trim Head (MED Shot of Simon)
5)	798+13		No Change

OLD LFOA 908+05   NEW LFOA 916+06   TOTAL CHANGE +8+01

The following are explanations for each of the five changes that appear on the film-change note.

1) The first note indicates that there are no changes from the first frame of action, FFOA, until the second note.

2) The second note indicates that at 567+09, 1+06 has to be trimmed from the tail of the A side, or outgoing shot. Eliminating 1+06 at the location 567+09 will remove the remainder of the A-side shot. Once the tail has been removed from the A side, the B side, or incoming shot, now begins at 567+09. Some people may like to include an optional note here that indicates that no changes now occur from 567+09 until the next change.

3 & 4) The next two changes are linked together. The first change is the addition of a new shot. The note indicates that a new shot is inserted at 789+01. This change adds 9+12 to the total length of the reel. The next shot, the medium shot of Simon, which was located at 789+01, is pushed later in the reel by 9+12 feet. The second portion of this change affects the Simon shot that we just moved. The head of this shot has to be trimmed by 0+05 frames. Once you have removed five frames from the head of the Simon shot, you will notice that the Simon shot still starts at 798+13; it's just a little shorter. The total length of the reel has been shortened by five frames and the starting footage for each subsequent shot in the reel begins five frames earlier.

5) The final change note indicates that starting at 798+13, there are no more changes. However, the fourth and fifth change notes may seem to contradict each other. Note #4 and note #5 both have 798+13 listed in the footage column. However, note #5 merely indicates that once the five frames have been removed in #4, there are no more changes from the head of that shot to the end of the reel.

The Footer

You should list the old and new length of the reel somewhere on the page in addition to the total footage difference for that particular reel. Simply add or subtract all the changes and apply that amount to the old LFOA, "last frame of action." In the example shown here, more footage is added than deleted. If you subtract all the deletions from the 9+12 addition, you get the total amount added to the reel. This amount can then be added to the old LFOA to give you the new LFOA. Some people subtotal the change lengths at the foot of each page on longer film-change notes.

It is extremely important that all changes are made in the order they appear on the film-change note. Change notes must be read in sequential order. Each change creates a ripple effect that alters the exact location of each subsequent shot.

CHAPTER 19
THE FILM WORLD

CHAPTER OUTLINE

Film Glossary
Script Supervising Glossary
   Continuity
   One-Line Continuity

I have met countless people who say they know how to use Media Composer or Xpress and they just want to quickly learn Film Composer. They usually say something like, "Oh, it's the same thing" or "If I know one, I know the other." The truth is, the Composer window interfaces are very similar to the 24-frame and 30-frame Composers. However, without an extensive working knowledge of film, an Avid assistant is not a valuable asset to a feature cutting room.

The following glossary provides succinct definitions and explanations of some useful items you may find in a feature-film editing room.

FILM GLOSSARY

AB REELS - Two 10-minute reels of a movie are often combined into a single reel known as an "AB Reel." A 10-reel movie can be condensed into five larger and longer AB reels. These reels are important when thinking about a mix. Sound mixers dub feature films using AB reels. Some theaters require that you build individual reels into larger AB reels for screenings. Remember to place changeovers at the end of each even-numbered AB reel for screenings.

Composer will perform sluggishly while playing sequences longer than ten minutes. However, you can combine your sequences together into one long, two-hour sequence for outputting purposes as long as your computer has enough available RAM.

BAR CODE - When raw film stock is manufactured, bar-code numbers are branded on the edge of the film. These numbers remain on the processed negative and also appear

183

on the workprint. They contain the same information as indicated by the key numbers but are intelligible to bar-code-reader machines.

BENCH - The work table for assistant editors. This is your desk, rewind table, syncing table, conforming table. It is also used for paperwork and working lunches.

BIN - A large container used to temporarily store strips of picture and track. A bin looks like a cloth-lined trashcan with a bar of tiny metal spokes that runs along the top of the bin for hanging film.

CAMERA REPORTS - Camera reports are documents created by the camera department during the shoot. One report is filled out for each exposed roll of film. They usually contain the following information:

- camera roll #
- scene & take
- notes
- length of shot in feet and total footage per roll
- frame rate
- date
- camera operator and/or assistant camera operator
- and the circled takes

The camera department hands in copies of the camera reports to the lab with the exposed camera rolls. The lab uses the circled take information on the camera reports to determine which takes to print. The editing room should receive a copy of every camera report.

CAMERA ROLL - Camera roll refers to a roll of exposed film used in motion picture cameras. They come in some standard lengths: 100 ft., 400 ft., and 1,000 ft. Camera operators may use very short portions of rolls, less than 100 ft. Portions of rolls are known as "short ends."

CHANGEOVERS - Small marks made on a print indicating the end of a reel. While screening multiple reels in a dual-projector screening room, you should place changeover marks near the end of the reel to indicate to the projectionist that the end of the reel is approaching. This will signal the projectionist to be ready to switch from one projector to the other. Changeover marks are placed 1 foot and 12 feet before the last frame of picture. The marks are small dots or slashes that appear in the top right of the screen. They can be applied to the print with a grease pencil, dot stickers, or paper tape.

While at the movies, you have probably seen changeover marks flash in the top right of the screen every twenty minutes. You probably will not see them on television due to the cropping that occurs during the film-to-television conversion.

CIRCLED TAKES - Circled takes are the preferred takes usually chosen by the director. The director picks circled takes on set for the purpose of informing the lab which takes to print. While screening dailies, the director may make another choice of circled takes from the available footage. You may want to identify circled takes in a Avid bin by adding a * to the clip name. Any footage that was not circled or printed is known as "b-neg." This material can be printed and transferred in telecine at a later date.

ECCO - A brand name for film cleaner. Some film cleaners are highly toxic. Less dangerous cleaning fluids are available. Whichever you prefer, always use in a well-ventilated space. If you experience dizziness or headaches due to toxic film cleaners, discontinue use immediately. It ain't worth it!

EDGE-CODE NUMBERS (a.k.a. Ink Numbers, Acmade Numbers, or Code Numbers) - Edge-code numbers are small numbers that are printed on the edge of both picture and track by an Acmade coding machine. The purpose of edge-code numbers is to ensure proper sync between picture and track. Once dailies have been synced up, an identical edge-code number is placed on the picture (from the start mark) as is placed on the track, allowing a sync point to be found very easily at all times. Edge-code numbers may be included in log-file and burn-in information.

After dailies have been synced up, the picture and track are edge-coded with corresponding numbers on a coding machine. These edge numbers allow the workprint and mag to be easily placed in sync.

If you are using edge-code numbers in your log-file and burn-in information, you must indicate to the telecine house the appropriate starting edge-code number for each dailies roll.

FLANGE - Half of a split reel. It is used for temporarily spooling small amounts of picture and track.

FLASH FRAME - A motion-picture film camera runs at 24 fps. At the beginning or end of a shot, as the camera speeds up to 24 fps or slows to a halt, more light is allowed through the shutter, overexposing the film. At a full stop, the frame remaining in the gate is completely exposed. On the negative, this frame appears black. On the work print, this frame appears clear. This clear frame is known as a "flash frame." One generally appears between each take in which the camera was stopped.

GANG SYNCHRONIZER - A metal device that locks picture and track into a roller system that maintains all elements in sync. A synchronizer can be equipped with one, two, or three sound heads. These sound heads, when connected to an amplifier, reproduce the audio from the mag. The Avid has a similar tool that locks the material in the record monitor to the material in the source monitor.

GANG SYNCHRONIZER BUTTON

GLOVES - White cotton gloves worn by film assistants in order to keep the film clean and free of fingerprints.

GREASE PENCIL - A wax pencil used to mark picture.

HOLE PUNCH - A single-hole punch is used for punching a hole on the punch frame on the workprint.

IP / IN - An interpositive (IP) is a positive image that is printed on negative stock. Opticals are made from IPs. An internegative (IN) is a negative made from a positive print.

KEY NUMBERS - When raw film stock is manufactured, key numbers are branded on the edge of the film. These numbers remain on the processed negative and appear on the workprint.

LAB REPORTS - The processing lab creates a document known as the lab report. This report includes the following information:

- camera roll #
- date
- lab roll #
- starting key #
- timing lights

(See Lab Reports, Chapter 6, **Film Dailies**.)

LOUPE - A small magnifying glass used to examine film.

PICTURE - The stuff you thread into a projector. The term "picture" transcends the film, video, and digital worlds.

PUNCH FRAME - The "punch frame" is the first A frame of each shot. Some telecine houses punch a hole in the negative at the head of every take. They use this sync point as a reference for telecine purposes. More commonly, while building and logging film dailies, the assistant editors punch a hole in the first frame of each shot on the work print, indicating the decisive start of the shot.

REELS – Full-length feature films are edited into approximately 10-minute sections called "reels." The longer the film, the more reels you have. A standard 35mm reel lasts approximately 10 or 11 minutes, or 1,000 feet. This protocol remains important for digital projects. In your project, create individual 10-minute sequences that, strung together, consist of all the material in your edited movie. Add Academy leader at the head and tail of each sequence.

REWIND - A metal crank with one handle and a long spoke that holds film reels. There are two rewinds mounted on the top of a film bench. Reels can be mounted on either rewind and spooled from one to the other. One of the rewinds should be able to swivel in order to wind film to and from a bin.

Just for fun, ask a novice apprentice editor to find you a left-handed rewind.

SHOT CARDS - Shot cards are index cards with each scene number and a very brief scene description. Most feature cutting rooms have a large board on the wall for displaying all the shot cards in rows corresponding to the reel in which they occur.

SOUND REPORTS - Sound reports are documents created by the sound mixer during the shoot. One report is filled out for each sound roll recorded. They usually contain the following information:

- sound roll #
- scene & take
- notes
- SMPTE timecode
- date
- name of the sound mixer
- the circled takes

The sound department hands in copies of the sound reports to the transfer house with the sound rolls. The editing room should receive a copy of every sound report.

SOUND ROLL - Location sound is recorded onto sound rolls, which come in different formats. Location sound mixers record onto either analog or digital formats. The Nagra sound recorder has been the preferred analog recorder for the past fifty years. It uses ¼-inch magnetic tape on a spool. Digital recorders are now becoming more popular. Some location sound mixers use Digital Audio Tape (DAT) recorders for location sound recording. DAT machines use small DAT-tape cassettes; however, they are sometimes still referred to as sound rolls.

SPACER - A small disc used to create a space between multiple reels on a single rewind when the work picture and mag track are not the same thickness. Therefore, a 1,000-ft. roll of picture will not have the same circumference as a 1,000-ft. roll of mag. As a result, when spooling picture and track from one rewind, through a synchronizer, to another rewind, an unevenness may occur, creating slack in the picture or the track that will start to tangle. Placing a spacer directly before and after the first reel on the take-up rewind will help prevent slack.

SPLICER - A cutting device that splices film and mag. It aligns picture or track, allowing for clean cuts and easy splicing.

SPLICING - Taping picture or track together. In the digital world, there are insert splices and overlay splices. Insert splices add material at a specific point while sliding the subsequent shots later. Insert edits change the length of a sequence. Overlay splices lay material over existing shots and do not necessarily affect the length of a sequence.

SPLICING TAPE - Clear splicing tape, perforated top and bottom, is used to splice the work picture. White splicing tape, perforated top and bottom, is used to splice mag track.

SPLIT REEL - A film reel that can be unscrewed into two halves. Rolls of film are mounted onto split reels for use on a bench.

SPRING CLAMP - A small spring coil used to hold reels tightly on a rewind.

SQUAWK BOX - A small amplifier used to produce the sound from the sound heads on a synchronizer.

TAILS OUT/HEADS OUT - A reel with the beginning or head on the outside of the roll is "heads out." If the reel needs to be rewound before watching it or listening to it, it's "tails out." (I often find it amusing to ask a young apprentice editor to please rewind all the reels in the Avid.)

TELECINE LOGS - A telecine log is a hard-copy print of the telecine's log files that is sent to the editing room with the dailies tape and log file.

TRACK - Mag or magnetic audiotape used as the sound element. It comes in the same size and shape as the picture except it is usually brown and opaque. Mag has a shorter lifespan than the workprint due to normal wear, play, and stretching. Audio channels in a digital editing system are referred to as tracks.

> **Different types of mag track:**
> Single-Stripe can accommodate one audio track and one balanced track for timecode.
>
> Three-Stripe can accommodate up to three tracks of whatever combination of audio and timecode.
>
> Full Coat (gray, opaque) can accommodate up to six tracks of whatever combination of audio and timecode.
>
> Mag track is manufactured on either acetate (most popular) or polyester (cheaper and won't tear).

VELVET - A black piece of velvet material used to clean film.

WORKPRINT - The positive picture image created from the original negative at the lab.

SCRIPT SUPERVISING GLOSSARY

DAILY SCRIPT SUPERVISOR NOTES - Daily script supervisor reports detail what was shot for a particular day. The report indicates whether a scene was completed, indicates incomplete scenes, and calculates the portion of the script shot compared to the balance remaining, and includes any other pertinent information.

FACING PAGES - Facing pages are created by the script supervisor on the set each day. They get their name because they lie opposite the lined script page on the back side of the previous page in the script-notes book. Facing pages contain information corresponding to the opposite lined-script page. These pages contain the following information:

- location & date
- scene & take
- circled take
- description & notes
- type of shot
- length of shot
- characters involved
- and director's comments

LINED SCRIPT - The script supervisor marks pages in the script with vertical lines indicating which scenes and takes have been shot. A vertical line through the page indicates which material is covered within each shot. A vertical wavy line indicates material that is covered in a scene, but the actors' lines are off-camera.

SCRIPT NOTES - The script supervisor (a.k.a. script super or continuity) is the main communication channel between the set and the editing room. The script supervisor prepares notes for every scene, take, and shot while on the set. These script notes contain important information for organization during the postproduction process. Script notes usually contain three main elements: the lined script, facing pages, and daily script supervisor notes.

Continuity

Continuity is a term that is widely used on motion-picture and television productions. In it purest form, the continuity person on the set, usually referred to as the script supervisor, is responsible for maintaining consistency in detail on the set. They make sure the actors are wearing the correct clothing for a scene and the set is prepared properly according to the script. They are responsible for making sure the actors deliver the appropriate line reading throughout a scene. If a scene was shot in portions at different times, the continuity person would check that the actors maintain consistent positions to match the previous takes in that particular scene. One common situation that many films fail to coordinate flawlessly is the position of cigarettes in actors' hands. If you watch movies closely, you can often notice cigarettes switching from one hand to another or burning down only to magically extend to almost new again.

One-Line Continuity

A one-line continuity is a document that summarizes the contents and length of each scene of a movie. It briefly describes, in one sentence, the contents of each scene, which reel the scene appears in, and the individual and combined lengths of each scene and reel. It is useful for organizing, on paper, the length of individual scenes, reels, and the entire movie.

CHAPTER 20
PREVENTIVE MAINTENANCE

CHAPTER OUTLINE

MAINTENANCE SCHEDULE

A healthy Avid is a happy Avid. Many computer-related problems such as crashing, sluggishness, and file corruption are preventable by following a rigorous system-maintenance regime. The plan is to eliminate any problems before they happen. The following is a recommended schedule of procedures you should perform to ensure a healthy and happy Avid.

MAINTENANCE SCHEDULE

Once a Day
Back up your project
(See Chapter 13, *Saving Your Work*)

Once a Week
Rebuild the desktop
Rebuild the Media Database files
Run Speed Disk on the hard drive
Run Norton Disk Doctor on all drives
Dump the MC State settings
Dump the DigiSetup file

Once a Month
Delete superfluous rendered effect media
Clean your hardware

WARNING! Always back up all your files, documents, and applications before performing any maintenance.

Rebuilding the Desktop

The desktop contains hidden information used by your computer to identify and locate data on the desktop. As you use your computer, changes to this information are made every second. Therefore, it is recommended that you rebuild the desktop files once a week or when any new drives are added to your system.

STEP BY STEP

1) Hold down the ⌘ and Option keys while you start your computer.

2) A dialog box will prompt you to rebuild the desktop. Click OK for each partition on the desktop.

TIP: You may also use Tech Tool to rebuild the desktop. This simple drive utility can rebuild the desktop.

Rebuilding the Media Database Files

The media database file is the only non-media file contained within each media drive. This small data file is the road map used by the software to find where each individual piece of media lives. As media is digitized to a drive, the media database rewrites itself. Similarly, if you delete or move media from a drive, the media database rewrites itself to indicate the changes in the contents of that drive.

This busy media database file may become corrupt. Corrupt media database files can prohibit the Composer software from launching. Deleting corrupt media database files may correct this problem. However, proper maintenance of your media database files will decrease the chances of corruption. Therefore, it is recommended that you delete the media database files weekly and rebuild them.

The media database has changed slightly in Composer version 7.0 and later. The function is similar, but the information is stored in a pair of files rather than just one file. The new design allows Composer to launch more quickly. One other difference is that the newer files have less-intelligible names.

MEDIA DATABASE FILES SINCE 7.0

Name	Size
msmMac.pmr	136K
msmOMFI.mdb	544K

REBUILDING MEDIA DATABASE FILES
STEP BY STEP

1) Close all software programs.

2) Open each media file folder on the media drives. Find the media database file (there is one in each partition of a media drive).

3) Drag each media database file into the trash and empty the trash.

4) Launch the Composer software.

If a media database file does not exist on a media drive while initializing the Composer software, the Avid is forced to rebuild the missing file. This process may take a while, depending on the density and quantity of media drives connected to your computer. You may decide to perform this maintenance overnight.

TIP: If you are on a SCSI MediaShare project, you can use the MSScanner software to instantaneously delete all media database files. You can do this by selecting Delete Media File DBs from the ScanVolume menu.

Optimizing Your Hard Drive

Optimizing is to a computer what a tune-up is to a car. A computer is a complex machine with an electrical system, a cooling system, and several moving parts. Care and attention is required to maintain a healthy computer. This does not mean that a well-kept computer will never fail, but preventive maintenance is the best way to ensure a dependable machine.

Your computer's brain exists almost entirely within the System Folder on the hard drive. The System Folder supplies the basic operating functions of a computer. The hard drive that contains the System Folder is known as the *startup disk*.

You *cannot* properly optimize a hard drive while it is in use. To optimize your hard drive, it is necessary to start up your computer from an alternate startup disk. While your computer is on, the startup disk is constantly in use and can't thoroughly examine areas of itself while it is busy performing the basic functions of a computer. Therefore, it is necessary to disengage the hard drive, leaving it dormant while you perform a complete diagnostic evaluation and treatment.

You may use a Zip disk, a Jazz disk, or a media drive as an alternate startup disk while performing maintenance, *as long as there is a System Folder and Norton Utilities installed on the device.*

Norton Utilities contains two very handy programs, Disk Doctor and Speed Disk (see Disk Doctor later in this chapter). Speed Disk optimizes information on a hard drive by rearranging the data into more-accessible and less-fragmented patterns. This process is called defragmenting. After a period of time of writing new information and deleting material from your hard drive, the drive may perform sluggishly. Speed Disk examines the selected drive, locates all the data, and rearranges the information into less scattered patterns. This process actually moves data from one part of the drive to another, which enables the computer to access the information more efficiently.

> **WARNING!** Do not operate Speed Disk on media drives. Media files are too large for Speed Disk to rearrange. Running Speed Disk on a media drive may result in loss of media, drive damage, or system failure.

> **WARNING!** Always back up all your files, documents, and applications before performing any maintenance.

DEFRAGMENTING FROM A ZIP OR JAZZ DISK
The following applies to defragmenting from a Zip disk.

STEP BY STEP

1) Insert the Zip disk into the Zip drive.

2) Copy your Avid's System Folder and a copy of Norton Utilities onto a Zip disk.

3) In your System Folder on your hard drive, open Control Panels and select Startup Disk. Change the startup disk from your hard drive to the Zip disk.

4) Restart the computer with the Zip disk inserted in the Zip drive. If the computer tries to spit out the Zip disk, push it back in immediately. It's like spoon-feeding medicine to a kid.

5) The computer should start up using the System Folder on your Zip disk. If you get an error message, your startup disk may not contain the correct system software version to operate your computer.

6) Open Speed Disk on the Zip disk and defragment your hard drive.

7) Change the startup disk from the alternate startup disk back to the original hard drive and restart the computer. The Zip disk should pop out automatically.

DEFRAGMENTING FROM A DRIVE
STEP BY STEP

1) Copy your System Folder and Norton Utilities onto an external drive. You may use any partition on a tower, fixed drive, or R-Mag as an alternate startup disk.

2) In your System Folder on your hard drive, open Control Panels and select Startup Disk. Change the startup disk from your hard drive to the partition, which now contains a copy of your system folder and Speed Disk.

3) Restart the computer.

4) Open the partition that contains a copy of your System Folder and Speed Disk.

5) Open Speed Disk and defragment your hard drive.

6) Change the startup disk from the alternate startup disk back to the original hard drive and restart the computer.

TIP: Make sure to unlock all drives before performing any maintenance. A locked drive will prevent a utility application from fixing any problems.

Regular Checkups At The Doctor (HIGHLY RECOMMENDED)

Norton Utilities contains the program Disk Doctor. Disk Doctor examines and fixes certain problems on computer drives. After a period of time of writing new information and deleting material from a drive, items may become corrupt, damaged, misplaced, missing, or obsolete. Disk Doctor examines the selected drive, analyzes all the data, and repairs most drive problems. This process enables the computer to perform more efficiently.

Running Norton Disk Doctor is not only a good course of preventive maintenance, it is a necessity on digital editing systems.

Run Disk Doctor on your hard drive from an alternate startup disk, such as a Zip disk, Jazz disk, or an external drive. You *cannot* properly optimize a hard drive while it is in use. Optimizing your hard drive requires starting your computer from an alternate startup disk. Follow the *same* instructions for running Disk Doctor as you would for running Speed Disk. Also run Disk Doctor on all media drives. This process may take a while, depending on the density and quantity of media drives connected to your computer. You may decide to perform this maintenance overnight.

TIP: Open the Norton Disk Doctor preferences from the Edit menu and select Fix Automatically. Also activate all the Option's check boxes. You can leave Disk Doctor running during lunch or overnight to automatically fix any problems. When Disk Doctor finishes examining the drives, a status report will appear letting you know what occurred.

TIP: Running Norton Disk Doctor every night may be necessary on SCSI MediaShare shows with Composer versions above 6.0. Norton will prevent inconsequential disk problems from developing into disasters. Make sure to unlock all drives before performing any maintenance. A locked drive will prevent a utility application from fixing any problems.

WARNING! There are problems with certain versions of the Composer software involving SCSI MediaShare. You may experience problems such as partitions dropping off the desktop, frequent corruption on media drive directories, or crashing due to software bugs. The Mount All function has become inoperative in some 6.0 versions. Using this function has even led to severe corruption in media-drive directories. In later versions of Composer 6.5, the Mount All function on the File menu has been deactivated. Avid's suggested work-around requires that you mount partitions using AVIDdrive Utility or by restarting the computer. Avid resolved this issue in Composer 7.0. In the interim, run Norton on all partitions overnight, with the Auto Fix and Bad Blocks preferences activated, for MediaShare projects.

WARNING! Always backup all your files, documents, and applications before performing any maintenance.

Rebuild the MCState Settings Files

MCState files are documents that contain Composer settings information. These settings files may become corrupt or damaged. Dump the MCState settings once a week as a course of preventive medicine. You will not lose any important information by trashing these files. At most, Composer will not remember which user setting or project was used last. Rebuilding the MCState file may eliminate some unexplained Composer anomalies.

STEP BY STEP

1) Remove the MCState file from the Settings folder in the Composer software folder.

2) Place the MCState file in the Trash and empty the Trash.

3) Start up the Composer software. The settings file will rebuild automatically.

Rebuilding the DigiSetup File

The DigiSetup file is a document that contains Composer audio calibration information. This file may become corrupt or damaged and should be trashed once a week. Rebuilding the Digi file may eliminate some unexplained audio anomalies.

STEP BY STEP

1) Remove the DigiSetup file from the Preferences folder in the System Folder. Depending on your Composer version, the DigiSetup file may be located either in the System Folder or the Preferences folder within the System Folder.

2) Place the DigiSetup file in the trash and empty the trash.

3) Start up the Composer software. The settings file will rebuild automatically.

Older versions of Composer utilize the Pro Tools calibration tool for rebuilding DigiSetup files.

Deleting Superfluous Rendered-Effect Media

Media is created when you render an effect. Old rendered effects that were removed from your sequence have not been completely eliminated, just hidden from view. The old media from these unused effects still exists on your drive. As the show progresses, the quantity of superfluous rendered effects increases. Deleting unnecessary media benefits the Avid by reducing the total number of objects in the project, increasing drive space, and speeding the process of rebuilding the media database files.

STEP BY STEP

1) Open the Cuts bin.

2) Under the bin's hamburger menu, select Set Bin Display and activate Show reference clips and Effects. The bin will now display all the effects associated with the sequence in the bin.

```
┌─────────────────────────────────────┐
│ Display Bin Selector                │
├─────────────────────────────────────┤
│   ▭  ⊠ Master Clips                 │
│   ▯  ⊠ Sub Clips                    │
│  ▦  ⊠ Sequences                    │
│   ◈  ☐ Sources                      │
│   ◪  ⊠ Effects                      │
│   ◿  ☐ Motion Effects               │
│   ✑  ☐ Rendered Effects             │
│  ▦  ☐ Groups                       │
├─────────────────────────────────────┤
│ ⊠ Show clips created by user        │
│ ⊠ Show reference clips              │
└─────────────────────────────────────┘
```

Your bin does not automatically display reference clips or effects. These items can be activated through the bin display settings.

3) Highlight the sequence and activate Select Media Relatives from the bin's hamburger menu. All the rendered effects that belong in the sequence will highlight. The effects icons that are not highlighted do not currently live in the sequence and are superfluous rendered effects.

4) Select Reverse Selection from the bin's hamburger menu to highlight all the superfluous rendered effects.

5) Delete the superfluous rendered effects.

WARNING! Deleting superfluous rendered effects from one bin may affect other sequences and alternate cut versions in different bins. Be careful when deleting superfluous rendered effects not to remove essential material from your project. You may want to place all your cuts in one bin and highlight all the media relatives from the media tool before deleting any superfluous rendered effects.

Cleaning Your Avid

Your computer and drives contain internal cooling fans that help prevent them from burning out. However, just as the ceiling fan in your home will accumulate a thick layer of disgusting gray fuzz if you don't clean it, so will the fans in the computer and drives.

The fans in your equipment are usually blowing out warm air from inside the casings of the equipment. Therefore, there must be a vent for air intake somewhere on the case. It should be easy to find due to the gray, fuzzy moss blocking the entrance.

If you are a real tech-head, turn off all power to these devices, open the casings, and remove the dust. Otherwise, call an authorized Avid technician to unblock the air vents in your Avid.

ADVANCED SERVICING TECHNIQUES

I have encountered countless glitches, bugs, unexplained phenomena, and mysterious quirks while trying to master the Avid. Not all problems will be prevented by performing a thorough maintenance regimen. The system will challenge your knowledge, question your judgment, and try your patience by acting like a spoiled child one minute and a crafty adversary the next. Most of the time, you will know why a problem arises. Sometimes, however, there may be no explanation for the enigma before you.

Assessing the Situation

I liken an Avid user to a triage doctor: You are faced with a set of symptoms and you have to investigate the source of the problem. Most times, if you trace the source of the problem, you will find a logical explanation. Do not be concerned if you can't explain why the system is malfunctioning. Many times the system just goofs up (this is a highly technical computer term). Shutting down the system and rebooting may be the only solution for restoring sanity to the Composer software. The longer you work with digital editing systems, the more familiar you will become with their quirks.

When the system malfunctions, crashes, or freezes, assess the symptoms and ask yourself the following questions:

1) What did I just do that made the machine mad? Try to determine if the function you are trying to perform is causing the problem. The system may malfunction due to something you have just done. I once had a sequence that caused the system to crash each time I tried to play it. I finally decided to duplicate the sequence and place the brand-new copy in a brand-new bin. The new copy of the sequence played perfectly fine in the new bin.

2) What is the machine trying to tell me? Read the machine's error messages and try to interpret their meaning. You may be trying to perform something that is not possible because of the configuration of your project. I once had a situation where the system refused to create titles. The system was not malfunctioning in that circumstance—the compression setting had been changed to an alternate AVR, which was preventing me from making a title.

3) Why is the machine acting strange? Take a step back and analyze what is happening not only to your machine but to all the devices attached to the system. The Avid is attached to a variety of different drives, decks, and devices that may affect its performance. On a shared storage show, adjoining systems may cause each other to act peculiarly. If one system crashes, it may disturb the adjoining system.

The following section explains some maintenance operations you should perform on your computer. They may be helpful if you experience a problem.

Startup Keyboard Functions

You can perform several preventive-maintenance techniques as you start up your computer. The following chart details a few helpful keystroke functions. Each keystroke combination should be held down while the computer starts up until a dialog box indicates that the function has been initiated.

FUNCTION	KEYSTROKE
Rebuild The Desktop	⌘–Option
Customize Extension Manager	Space Bar
Turn Extensions Off	Shift
Zap The P-Ram	Option–⌘–P–R

• Rebuilding the desktop refreshes the computer's understanding of what is sitting on the desktop.

• Customizing the extensions manager allows you to select the necessary extensions from a menu while the computer is booting up.

• Turning the extensions off eliminates conflicting extension problems, allowing you to isolate a problem.

• Zapping the P-Ram, "the computer enema," resets many general computer settings. After performing a zap, reset the Control Panel items.

MOB

Master clips and subclips contain additional data that does not exist in the bin, is not visible on the burn-in, and is not listed on the Finder level. This hidden information is known as the Media Object (MOB). The MOB is Avid's way of branding each clip with its own unique identifying mark.

During the course of a project, clips are duplicated, moved from one workstation to another, and modified. If you duplicate a clip and move the copy into a new open bin, changes to the original clip will automatically update the copy. The Composer software maintains that clips with identical MOBs keep the same information. This natural occurrence does not work across shared-storage systems because each station is not necessarily privy to changes within another project. The danger arises when clips and their clones begin to differ. An original clip that originates in one workstation may be copied to multiple other workstations. If the original clip is modified in some way by changing the sound-timecode numbers or key numbers, for example, the copies, or clones, will not match the original clip. An outdated and inaccurate copy of a clip, when transported back to a workstation, may unknowingly update not only any other copies of the original clip but the original clip itself.

If you move a sequence from a workstation that has outdated clips associated with that sequence, the destination workstation's clips may default to the outdated clips once you open the bin containing the sequence. Generating a cut list or EDL from this sequence will access the associated outdated and inaccurate clips.

You can take certain precautions to prevent losing clip information:

Always retain a copy of the original clip in your project. In the event that you lose clip information, you can refer to the original master clip. Also, make sure that you do not have mutated versions of the same clip floating around.

Try to modify and/or add information to a clip before you copy it or move it.

Duplicate clips using ⌘–D rather than Option+dragging. Duplicating creates a new clip with a different MOB and will be less likely to update the clip it originated from.

Avoid duplicating bins and projects. Create new bins and new projects.

Relinking a sequence with outdated information to the original and accurate clips may update and correct the sequence.

Corrupt File Maintenance

New Project - Avid likes to recommend creating a new project as a means for solving almost any problem. In the rare event that your project has become corrupt, make a brand-new project and move all your bins into the new project. Remember to configure the project settings to match the old project.

New User - This is another one of Avid's favorite recommendations. If the user settings become corrupt, create a brand-new user and reconfigure all your settings. You can copy user settings from user to user or from a user to the site settings. Site settings can be copied to user settings. However, if the user settings are corrupt, it would be better to start from scratch.

> **WARNING!** You may experience problems while trying to use user settings that were created in an older version of the software. Do not use 6.0 user settings in any version of the 6.5 Composer software. Do not use 6.0 or 6.5 user settings with Composer 7.0. Reconfigure new user settings from scratch when upgrading Composer software.

Reinstall the System Software - The system software may become corrupt or damaged. System functions that start acting abnormal may indicate that the system software needs to be replaced. You probably do not have the system software disks in your cutting room. Ask your rental house or Avid technician to reinstall the system software or provide you with the disks to do it yourself.

TIP: You can start up your computer from the system software on a CD-ROM by holding down the C key as your computer boots up.

WARNING! Remember to reconfigure system settings if you reinstall system software.

Delete Creation Files - Occasionally, the Avid will create superfluous files that appear in the media file folders. These files are an indicator that a problem has already occurred and been solved. These files, named "creation files," must be deleted. It is a good idea to periodically perform a Find to search for creation files.

Remove Dump Files - Sometimes when an Avid crashes, the system will display a dialog box with three options: Continue, Exit To Finder, or Create A Report. If you select the later, the system will create a Dump file and store it in the Composer software folder. Dump files are only useful for telling you why the system crashed. Most of the time the information is incomprehensible. If you have already read the Dump file or don't really care what it says, remove it from the Composer software folder.

DUMP FILES

     ☐ Dump 1997/03/22 10.22.15

     ☐ Dump 1997/03/22 15.50.57

     ☐ Dump 1997/03/22 15.52.04

     ▪ MC6.5v5_PCI

In Composer versions since 7.0, the Avid creates a Fatal Errors folder, which lives next to the Composer software that contains Dump files and other error reports. This folder should be emptied periodically.

FatalErrorReports

CHAPTER 21

THE KITCHEN SINK

CHAPTER OUTLINE

Troubleshooting

TROUBLESHOOTING

Now that you completely understand the Avid, here are a few more little bits of information you might find useful.

PROBLEM: A dialog box with an Error 36 appears.
SOLUTION: Error 36 messages usually indicate a SCSI-chain problem. Unfortunately the error encompasses a wide range of hardware-connection problems. Check all your connections to and from the system. Try to isolate the problem by detaching one element at a time from your system. Replace old cables and terminators with new ones. Faulty storage expanders will also cause Error 36 messages. If you experience problems with drives attached to a storage expander, replace the unit immediately.

> **WARNING!** Always shut down the system before you attach, detach, or check any cable or device connection. Altering a hardware connection to a system that is on may cause a crash.

PROBLEM: A dialog box appears as the Composer software tries to launch.
ERROR MESSAGE

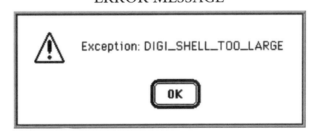

SOLUTION: Restart the entire system and try again. This annoying error message is one of many quirks associated with some of the more recent Composer versions.

PROBLEM: The Avid crashed.
SOLUTION: Don't panic. The Avid saves your material periodically (see Auto-Save, Chapter 13). If the left monitor has switched to Mac Bugs, a screen that looks like a white page with unintelligible information on the left side, try typing "es" and Enter to escape. If you are still frozen, type "rs" and Enter to do a soft restart. You may want to try to force-quit the program by keystroking ⌘–Option–ESC.

If nothing is responding, restart the computer by hitting Control–⌘–Start. If all else fails, press the restart button on the computer. This is called a hard restart or reboot. Unfortunately, you may have lost your work since the Avid saved last.

PROBLEM: There is no sound playing with the video.
SOLUTION: Make sure the pull-in switch is set to "x 0.99," not "x 1.00." Check that the frequency pull-in rate is set to the same position as when you digitized.

PROBLEM: While launching the Composer software, an error message warns you that the 3-D Hardware is not installed.
SOLUTION: Type "disable3d" in the composer's console to deactivate the systems from thinking that a 3D board should be attached.

FYI: The native port on the computer only supports up to AVR 3e. You can not digitize or access media at resolutions higher than AVR 3e from a media drive that is connected to the native port.

FYI: Editing in scrub mode with the Caps Lock key depressed sucks a lot of juice from the RAM, which slows the Composer software.

TIP: Hit the T key while rendering to display the estimated render-time duration in the dialog box.

TIP: An orange dot on an effect = real-time effect, a green dot = effect still has to be rendered, a blue dot = conditional.

Underrun Errors

One of the more common problems inherent in some Composer versions is the underrun error. This usually indicates that the system can not successfully play the required media due to a capacity overload. The audio or video media files may be too large, too complex, or stored improperly. Avid suggests (at high resolutions) storing audio and video media files in different partitions, and even drives, to help prevent underrun problems.

CHAPTER 22
THE UNIONS

A motion picture or television project can be categorized into one of two groups: non-union productions and union productions. Non-union productions may hire non-union or union members. Union productions are required to only hire union members except in the event that union members are not available, which rarely occurs. The motion picture and television industry relies heavily on union members. There are unions for actors, cinematographers, production designers, art designers, lighting technicians, drivers, builders, electricians, studio office support, security officers, projectionists, and editors, just to name a few.

The majority of motion pictures and television shows are produced in California. Most of the studio or larger-budget productions fall under the union umbrella while small or low-budget projects are often non-union. Joining a union provides you with the flexibility to work on either non-union or union productions.

UNION BENEFITS

Unions are designed to protect and serve their members. Unions establish minimum wage requirements, enforce fair and safe working environments, define daily work schedules in regards to required breaks and overtime, protect members from wrongful termination or abuse, support members in disputes, provide health coverage to members and their families, provide life insurance and pension plans, and list unemployed members on an availability roster.

LOCAL 700

For many years, there have been plans to unite the New York Editors Union (Local 771) with the Los Angeles chapter (Local 776). On September 18, 1998, the official result of a bicoastal editing-union members vote was announced in favor of this merger. In late 1998, the national committee approved this plan to combine the New York and Los Angeles Unions to form a new national editing union, Local 700.

Local 700 adopted all of the Local 776 rules and laws. Local 776 members experienced no change in benefits. The New York Local 771 members are now governed and protected under the new Local 700's constitution.

The following information details the eligibility requirements for the editing union in Los Angeles. This information has been obtained directly from the union and may be updated periodically. Please check with the union directly for the most up-to-date information.

MOTION PICTURE   EDITORS GUILD

Local 776
7715 Sunset Boulevard, Suite 200
Hollywood, CA 90046
(323) 876-4770 FAX (323) 876-0861

LOCAL 776

There are three ways to be placed on the Industry Experience Roster:

1. If qualified persons are not available to meet the employment requirements of the production company in any job classification (picture editor, sound editor, music editor, trailer editor, assistant editor, librarian, animation editor, technical director, and apprentice) and the company can satisfactorily demonstrate this, the company may then obtain employees from other sources.

2. If you are working for a non-signatory (non-union) employer and that employer becomes signatory (union) by signing the Basic Agreement, you will be eligible for roster placement after accumulating 30 consecutive work days with that signatory company.

3. By demonstrating **175 days** of work experience within a **three-year** period prior to the date of application in the classification of picture editor, music editor, or sound editor.

Or **100 days** of work experience within a **two-year** period prior to the date of application in the classification of animation editor, assistant editor, librarian, sound reader, technical director, or trailer editor.

All such work experience must be like the work covered by the Local 776 Agreement or Videotape Supplemental Agreement, and the work must have been performed in the 13 western states (Alaska, Arizona, California, Colorado, Hawaii, Idaho, Montana, Nevada, New Mexico, Oregon, Utah, Washington, Wyoming).

Documentaries, Industrial Films, and Educational Films are not covered by these agreements.

Roster placement for apprentice editors is limited to methods 1 and 2.

Union Wages

Minimum Wage Scales:	3/29/98-5/29/99	5/30/99-7/31/00
"ON CALL" EDITOR	$2,044.41	$2,105.74
5 consecutive days		
(doesn't include Golden Hours)		
SOUND EDITOR	$1,490.27	$1,534.98
Weekly guar. 48.6 hrs.	(30.664/hr.)	(31.584/hr.)
MUSIC EDITOR	$1,490.27	$1,534.98
Weekly guar. 48.6 hrs.	(30.664/hr.)	(31.584/hr.)
LIBRARIAN	$1,169.24	$1,204.32
Weekly guar. 43.2 hrs.	(26.099/hr.)	(26.882/hr.)
ASSISTANT EDITOR	$1,188.59	$1,224.25
Weekly guar. 45 hrs.	(25.023/hr.)	(25.774/hr.)
LIBRARIAN	$1,068.80	$1,100.86
Weekly guar. 43.2	(23.857/hr.)	(24.573/hr.)
EDITORIAL APPRENTICE	$882.62	$909.10
Weekly guar. 40 hrs.	(22.066/hr.)	(22.728/hr.)
TRAILER EDITOR	$1,368.79	$1,409.85
Weekly guar. 40 hrs.	(28.817/hr.)	(29.681/hr.)
ANIMATION EDITOR	$1,208.40	$1,244.64
Weekly guar. 40 hrs.	(30.210/hr.)	(31.116/hr.)

6th day payable @ 1 1/2 x (min. call 8 hrs.)
7th day payable @ 2 x (min. call 8 hrs.)
Vacation pay = 4% of weekly guarantee
Holiday pay = 3.719% of weekly guarantee

Union Holidays

New Year's Day	Labor Day
Washington's Birthday	Thanksgiving Day
Good Friday	Day after Thanksgiving
Memorial Day	Christmas Day
Independence Day	

Initiation Fees

Picture Editor	$3,000.00
Sound Editor	$2,000.00
Music Editor	$2,000.00
Technical Director	$1,500.00
Assistant	$1,500.00
Trailer Editor	$1,500.00
Animation Editor	$1,500.00
Apprentice Editor	$1,000.00
Sound Reader	$1,000.00

LOCAL 771

The Motion Picture Editors Local 771 I.A.T.S.E.
William R. Hanauer, Business Agent
Norman Gay, Asst. Business Agent
165 West 46 Street, Suite 900
New York, NY 10036-2501
(212) 302-0771 (212) 302-1091 FAX

Motion Picture Editors Local 771 of the International Alliance of Theatrical Stage Employees is the primary labor organization representing freelance and staff editing personnel on the East Coast. Local 771 negotiates and maintains contracts for its members who are employed throughout the motion picture and television industry on Feature Films, Documentaries, Commercial Spots, Corporate and Educational Industries, Music Videos, and Student Films.

Union Wages

EDITOR:	$1,912.50
SOUND, MUSIC, EFFECTS, ADR & DUBBING EDITOR:	$1,751.00
ASSISTANT EDITOR:	$1,138.50
EDITING ROOM ASSISTANT:	$ 650.00

Daily Rate: 25% of weekly gross wage.

Hours and Over Time: Time-and-one-half after eight (8) and forty (40) hours worked. Double-time after twelve (12) hours worked. Triple-time after sixteen (16) hours worked. Saturdays, Sundays, and Holidays worked are paid at double-time up to twelve (12) hours; triple-time after twelve (12) hours.

Vacation Pay: 4% of base wage rate paid at end of job.

Holidays: New Years Day, Lincoln's Birthday, Washington's Birthday, Memorial Day, Independence Day, Labor Day, Columbus Day, Veterans' Day, Thanksgiving Day, and Christmas Day.

Eligibility for Membership in Local 771

When applying for membership in this Local, you must reside within the Local's jurisdiction and meet one of the following requirements: (a) be employed in the craft, (b) have been employed in the craft, (c) show proof you will receive employment in the craft.

Initiation Fees and Dues

Upon making application to Local 771 and the IATSE, you pay 1/3 of the initiation fee as shown below, a quarterly service fee of 27% of one week's scale wage rate, and administrative fees of $65.00.

Initial Fees:		(1/3)
EDITOR	$2,700.00	$900
ASSISTANT EDITOR	$1,200.00	$400

The quarterly dues rate for Local 771 members is 27% of one week's scale wage rate for the classification in which you work.

MAKING YOUR DEAL

Non-union productions do not have any guidelines regarding pay scale or overtime pay. Unfortunately, non-union rates are often predetermined based on what the production has budgeted for editorial. Union productions are required to pay "scale."

Scale

The term scale refers to the minimum wage required by the union based for a standard work week. On a union project, you are either hired at scale or above scale. It is a common practice for union productions to sign you to an above-scale deal involving more money and more hours. The employer may offer to pay you more money if you agree to work five or ten more hours a week. At first glance, this weekly increase in wage may sound enticing. However, remember to do the math. Figure out what the difference is between scale and the wage offered. Then figure out what you would make if the extra hours would be paid at overtime. You may discover that you would be making more if you signed a scale deal.

There are three things your should remember while making your deal on a new project:

1) Don't be an egotist!
In this very competitive business—many qualified individuals may be competing for the same position. Anything can happen during the hiring and dealmaking process. Think about the big picture. If you are faced with a fiscal dilemma, try to keep in mind what is important. Avoid regrets by prioritizing, and stick to your convictions.

2) Don't be greedy!
Find out the fair market value. There may already be a standard established for the job you are applying for. Different studios may not pay the same amount for the same position. Some studios are known for paying slightly more or less than the standard. Don't price yourself out of the market. A potentially rewarding work experience may be more important than losing an opportunity over $50 a week.

3) Don't get screwed!
Be careful not to get caught in a lie regarding your rate. The production or studio you are negotiating with may contact your previous employer to establish your previous rate. Many postproduction supervisors keep in contact with each other and can easily find out somebody's rate history. Remind the employer not to compare apples to oranges. Working for two weeks at scale just to help a friend out by conforming a film does not automatically reduce your rate down to scale. Your previous body of work should determine your rate when negotiating a deal.

Box Kits

A "box kit" refers to any equipment an employee rents to his employer. Usually, production companies would rather rent equipment than purchase items they will have no use for once the project is over. If an employee owns equipment that the production company would normally have to rent from an outside vendor, they may chose to rent the equipment from you. Sometimes the production can save money if you rent your equipment for less than the market value. If you are a cinematographer who owns your own 35mm camera, the production may hire you along with your camera equipment. Some editors own their own digital editing systems and rent them for the duration of the show. Some assistant editors rent their personal computer to a production. Whatever you rent to the production should have no bearing on your rate and should not be used as a negotiating tool for the production to reduce your salary.

CHAPTER 23
AVID PRODUCTS

CHAPTER OUTLINE

In addition to the Film and Media Composer digital editing systems, Avid Technology offers an array of other editing, graphics, and effect programs. The following are a few of Avid's other products.

AVID XPRESS

The Avid Xpress (formerly MCXpress) is another of Avid's digital editing products. The Xpress is basically a junior Avid or "Avid Lite" as Brett Smith of New Media calls it. It is specifically designed for 30-fps video projects and closely resembles the Media Composer with fewer options and less flexibility. Xpress is completely compatible and upgradeable to any Media Composer.

Xpress can be used as an offline editing machine or a fully complete finishing system capable of EDL, direct output, and broadcast-quality two-field resolutions. In addition to the simplified hardware configuration with audio and video connections directly into the CPU, the Xpress software interface differs slightly from the Media Composer. Rather than a dual-monitor Composer window, footage is accessed through individual pop-up monitors. The editing functions are all found in a movable button palette.

Some of the Media Composer features that are absent in Xpress include decompose function, integrated two-monitor Composer interface, bin script view, stored bin heading views, and a customizable keyboard.

For more information on the Xpress system, contact New Media in Los Angeles, CA, at (323) 957-5000.

The following information has been provided, in part, by Avid.

AVID NEWSCUTTER

Avid NewsCutter is a nonlinear digital news-editing system. The latest version of the NewsCutter is the NewsCutter DV, the first DV-native, nonlinear Windows NT-based editing system designed specifically for news. The NewsCutter DV eliminates the linear restrictions of tape-based systems and offers editing flexibility on a PC platform. With Avid's DV-native solution, broadcasters acquiring media in a DV format have the ability to edit without dubbing back to tape or changing media formats, making DV production faster and easy-to-use with no generation loss.

AVID MEDIA ILLUSION

Avid Media Illusion is a digital nonlinear compositing solution for creating effects. Media Illusion merges paint, compositing, image manipulation, and special effects into one artistic domain. A powerful companion to Avid's editing systems, Media Illusion software complements your editing capabilities with the tools needed to complete even the most challenging effects work. With the latest version, artists can conform Media Composer sequences in the Media Illusion system using a familiar Avid timeline and the powerful Composition Link feature. Composition Link multilayered projects move seamlessly to Media Illusion, so edits are automatically recreated in any resolution. Users can digitize and assemble uncompressed source material in real time as well as automatically rebuild cuts, dissolves, and effects.

AVID MATADOR

Avid Matador is an open-platform paint application for the television, broadcast, and film markets. Matador combines painting, special effects, rotoscoping, tracking, and multi-layered 2D animation in one resolution-independent environment. Avid Matador software provides high-quality images with total resolution-independence and up to 64-bit color depth. The software's paint tools include a wide selection of user-configurable brushes, including a clone brush that offers quick, single-step duplication. Other features include an array of filters, vector shapes, and color-correction tools. Split-screen preview allows artists to accurately review and compare "before and after" color corrections. Artists can also generate macros so they can automate repetitive tasks. Avid Matador allows artists to generate masks from luminance, chroma, component, or hue. Matador's rotosplines automatically generate spline-based traveling mattes for fast, accurate effects. Users can also manage complex rotospline work with a timeline designed for control, allowing artists to control each rotospline shape individually as well as view all shapes together while treating any one.

AVID MARQUEE

Avid Marquee is a true 3D real-time text-creation tool. The simplified interface makes it fast for animators with no 3D experience to generate 3D text with lights and reflections. The same powerful texture mapping and light effects can be applied to 2D animation. Users can animate entire words or individual letters. Automatic nesting of letters in the timeline allows individual characters to be animated easily, and any property at any time can be animated via powerful timeline Bezier graphs. Users can animate kerning, extrusion, and texture-mapped images over time using five different curve types. All animations can be viewed instantly. Marquee not only provides property animation over time, but also the ability to trim the in-points and out-points of each segment. Marquee offers nonlinear editing for title animations, making for easier and more accurate timing of elements. And Marquee can also output over 25 different file formats for easy integration into other systems. It also supports Media Composer's AVR resolutions via OMFI for fast media exchange between the two applications.

CHAPTER 24

COMPOSER 8.0

CHAPTER OUTLINE

Sneak Preview of Media Composer 8.0

Now that you have read this book and you feel completely comfortable and up to speed with the new advances in fibre technology and Composer 7.0, take a moment to see what is in store for digital editing in the future. The following information has been provided, in part, by Avid.

SNEAK PREVIEW OF MEDIA COMPOSER 8.0

Avid Technology announced plans to release Media Composer Version 8.0 and a new model for shipment in 1999. The new model, Media Composer Online, features Avid's next-generation Meridien video subsystem and brings uncompressed images to Media Composer systems for the first time. The version 8.0 software release will provide a host of enhancements to the system's online editing capabilities, improved compatibility with other Avid products, and third-party solutions, as well as features to support film-based television projects.

The Meridien video board, which provides uncompressed real-time video streams and a downstream keyer, is capable of handling both uncompressed and a wide range of fixed kB/frame compressed video formats. It will support a single uncompressed stream of video on the MC Online model. The new hardware also includes a separate breakout box, allowing easy access to all I/Os, including serial digital, BetaCam, S-Video, and composite, as well as analog and digital audio.

Media Composer 8.0 will include Intraframe II, featuring shape-based color effects, enabling users to create shapes within the Intraframe Editing option and restrict color to specific areas for greater control over elements of an image.

Interoperability and Compatibility Features: Avid has created a new format for asset management, Open Media Management (OMM), that will provide access to production elements on shared storage. Customers using third-party asset-management products supporting OMM will be able to use the new format to retrieve, search, and manage graphics and media files between many applications.

Media Composer 8.0 supports QuickTime 3.0. Editors will be able to render using the Avid codec with QuickTime 3.0, allowing multimedia producers to use the new Sorenson codec to compress movies for distribution.

Media Composer 8.0 will be Avid's first implementation of the new format for metadata interchange. Advanced Authoring Format Version 1.0 (AAF) will be backward-compatible with OMFI, but as a new format, AAF contains more metadata than is possible with OMFI. AAF ensures Avid customers compatibility with third-party vendors supporting AAF, including Softimage, Digidesign, Adobe, Matrox, Pinnacle Systems, Sonic Foundry, and Truevision.

Media Composer's Automation Gain feature will be compatible with a wider range of third-party MIDI controllers. Autoconform Enhancements: Media Composer will support batch import of graphic and audio elements that do not come from a timecode source. As more and more elements are being created digitally, linking and importing will allow these elements to be used at any resolution during the creation and finishing stages of a program.

New AVX Plug-Ins applications from Hollywood FX, Transjammer, ICE, Ultimatte, Artel Software, Boris Effects, and DigiEffects will be available with Media Composer 8.0, along with a new version of AVX and other plug-ins still to be announced. Expect enhanced support for Film-Based Television and DTV Post Production.

Media Composer 8.0 will provide an important new feature for editing film-based television projects and fulfill HD/DTV programming delivery needs. A new Pan & Scan capability will allow users to edit projects originating from widescreen formats, such as film or HDTV or current anamorphic 601, for distribution on standard 4x3 television. Editors can interactively previsualize and select which portions of the composition are shown, and all creative decisions are automatically retained for direct machine-to-machine translation in the final film transfer. Version 8.0 software will support all of Avid's current PCI-based Media Composer models as well as the new Media Composer Online model.

THE POSTPRODUCTION PROCESS, A - Z

SHOOT FILM

PROCESS FILM - The film lab processes the negative.

LAB PRINTING - The lab makes one-light prints of all requested takes.

SOUND - Dub the location sound rolls to mag.

SYNC DAILIES - Sync the dailies before telecine.

EDGE-CODE FILM AND MAG - Either code the dailies before or after telecine.

TELECINE - Transfer the dailies to tape. Send a loop to the telecine house for sound calibration. Send framing leader to the telecine house prior to the first day of principal photography.

DIGITIZE - Digitize the telecine tapes into the digital editing system.

EDIT - Provide VHS copies of film as it progresses.

CONFORM PICTURE - Generate cut lists and change lists for conforming.

OUTPUT SOUND FROM AVID FOR SCREENING - Transfer Avid audio to mag at sound transfer house.

SCREEN EDITOR'S CUT - Bring a pillow.

RECONFORM PICTURE - Generate change lists.

RE-OUTPUT SOUND FROM AVID FOR SCREENING - Transfer Avid audio to mag at sound transfer house.

SCREEN DIRECTOR'S CUT - Take notes and try not to cry.

RECONFORM PICTURE - Generate change lists and conform the workprint.

TURN OVER TO SOUND - Provide the sound editors with EDLs, outputs, and sound cut lists.

TEMP DUB - The sound department performs a mini mix for the screening.

SCREEN FILM FOR STUDIO

MAKE MORE PICTURE CHANGES - Generate change lists and conform the workprint.

TURN OVER TO SOUND - Provide the sound editors with EDLs, outputs, and sound change lists.

TEMP DUB - The sound department performs a mini mix for the preview.

PREVIEW - Forget sleeping this week.

FINAL PICTURE CHANGES

LOCK PICTURE - Party Time!

FINAL CONFORM - Generate change lists and conform the workprint.

TURN OVER TO SOUND - Provide the sound editors with final EDLs, outputs, and sound cut lists.

SEND MPAA A COPY OF THE FILM - The MPAA assigns the movie rating.

SPOT FOR SOUND - Determine all the places where music and sound effects belong.

SOUND EDITING BEGINS

COMPOSER SCORES PICTURE - Hopefully in time for the mix.

GET MUSIC RIGHTS - All source music has to be cleared.

ORDER TITLES AND OPTICALS - Check the opticals before cutting them into the workprint.

MARK UP WORKPRINT - Place a "c" in grease pencil on each cut or run through marks for match cuts. This helps the negative cutter.

CUT NEGATIVE - Check the first answer print to make sure there are no mis-cuts.

TIME THE MOVIE - The color timers at the film lab make color corrections on the film.

FINAL MIX - Make a dirty-dupe copy of the workprint for the mix.

PRINT MASTER - Shoot the sound optical prints.

CHECK PRINTS - Someone has to check the prints for quality and mistakes.

APPENDIX B
EDITING EQUIPMENT LIST

FILM ROOM
Acetone _____
Acmade coder _____
Acmade coding tape: white, blue, black _____
Arch file clipboards, 2-ring legal _____
Architect tape - white _____
Bench stools w/back _____
Bench w/4 tier and rewinds
   (one rewind w/swivel base per bench) _____
Binders, 3 ring - 1" _____
Binders, 3 ring - 2" _____
Binders, 3 ring - 3" _____
Board, 6ft. x 4ft., cork or foam _____
Board, mark-n-wipe _____
Bulbs, low and reg. watts _____
Canned air _____
Chairs _____
China marker - white _____
China marker - yellow _____
Cores, 35mm, 3" _____
Corrugated boxes _____
Cotton-tip applicators _____
Desktop wire file-holder _____
Envelopes, #10 size _____
Envelopes, 11x14 mailing _____
Envelopes, legal size _____
Expo dry-erase eraser _____
Expo dry-erase marker set _____
Film cans _____
Film Horse _____
Film rack, 6-tier _____
Flange, 1,000ft. w/ key _____

Flatbed, Kem, 4 or 6 or 8 plate   _____

Extra Kem bulbs   _____

Gloves, large cotton   _____

Hanging folders, letter size   _____

Highlighter markers   _____

Hole puncher, 3-ring adjustable   _____

Hole puncher, 2-ring   _____

Hole puncher, single   _____

Index cards, 4x6 blue   _____

Index cards, 4x6 white   _____

Labels, Avery videotape labels   _____

Labels, dots   _____

Lamp, desk w/extending arm   _____

Legal pads, yellow   _____

Loupe   _____

Manila folders, letter size   _____

Masking tape   _____

Non-toxic film cleaner   _____

Notebook dividers pkgs., multi-colors   _____

Packing tape w/dispenser   _____

Pads, Post-It   _____

Pads, steno   _____

Paper clips   _____

Pencil sharpener, electric   _____

Pencils   _____

Pens, ball-point   _____

Phone message pads   _____

Plastic squeeze bottles   _____

Push pins   _____

Razor blades   _____

Reels, 1,000 split   _____

Reels, 2,000 split   _____

Rubber bands, #32 size   _____

Ruler, metal 18"   _____

Scissors   _____

Scotch tape dispenser   _____

Scotch tape   _____

Scribe   _____

Sharpies, extra fine: black, red, blue   _____

Sharpies, fine point: black, red, blue   _____

Spacer   _____

Splicer, Reva straight w/extender   _____

Splicer blade refills   _____

Splicing tape, film   ———
Splicing tape, track   ———
Spring clamps   ———
Squawk box   ———
Staple remover   ———
Stapler w/staples   ———
Stripping sleeves   ———
Synchronizer, 2-gang   ———
Synchronizer, 4-gang w/3 mag heads   ———
Tape dispenser, double   ———
Tape, paper - white 1", 3/4"   ———
Tape, paper - white 1/2", 1/4"   ———
Tape, paper - white, green, red, blue, orange 1/2"   ———
Tape, paper - white, green, red, blue, orange 1/4"   ———
Trim bins, large   ———
Trim boxes, large   ———
Trim tabs   ———
Velvet   ———
Webril wipes   ———
White Out   ———
Writing pad, spiral   ———

LEADER (painted) or (plastic)
Leader, white   ———
Leader, black   ———
Leader, yellow   ———
Leader, blue   ———
Leader, red   ———
Academy   ———
Focus chart   ———
Opaque leader   ———
Shot-missing slug   ———

AVID ROOM
Avid 9000 w/Film Composer   ———
Cassette player, stereo   ———
CD player, stereo   ———
DAT tapes   ———
Hi8 tapes   ———
Laser printer   ———
Monitor, NTSC 32"   ———
Printer paper   ———
Sony Beta SP deck   ———
Sony Beta SP videotapes 30 min., 60 min.   ———

Storage drives _____
UPS _____
VHS recorder, stereo _____
VHS stock 10, 30, and 120 min. _____
Zip or Jazz disks _____
Zip or Jazz drive _____

MISCELLANEOUS
Lamps _____
Microwave _____
Water cooler w/fridge _____

DIGITAL ASSISTANT'S TOOLBOX
Phillips screwdriver _____
Flathead screwdriver _____
Mini eyeglasses screwdriver _____
Headphones _____
Film calculator _____
Laptop computer _____
Utility software: Norton Utilities, Disk First Aid, Tech Tool _____
Avid user settings _____
System software _____
A copy of *The Avid Digital Editing Room Handbook* _____

APPENDIX C
HELPFUL PHONE NUMBERS

Apple	(800) 767-2775
Avid	(800) 800-2843
Claris	(408) 727-8227
Deluxe	(323) 462-6171
Digidesign	(800) 333-2137
Eagle Eye	(818) 506-6100
Local 776	(323) 876-4700
Local 771	(212) 302-0771
Teac	(323) 726-0303
Technicolor	(818) 769-8500
Transoft	(800) 949-6463
Unemployment (L.A.)	(323) 993-4600

INDEX

ABOUT THE AUTHOR

Born in Glasgow, Scotland, Tony Solomons moved to the United States in 1981. He completed his undergraduate studies in film at New York University and received a Master's degree in editing from the American Film Institute in Los Angeles. It was while Tony was teaching at the American Film Institute that he began writing this book. He continues to teach editing at the University of Southern California and work on the Avid in feature-film cutting rooms, and it is his dedication to the collaborative process of filmmaking that continues to inspire him in his work.